Jennie Wade

Riches of Grace

....A COLLECTION OF....

New Songs and Standard Hymns

—FOR THE USE OF—

Sunday-Schools, Devotional Meetings, Young People's Meetings, and other Services.

——BY——

E. S. LORENZ, CHAS. H. GABRIEL, W. A. OGDEN, J. H. TENNEY, ADAM GEIBEL, AND GEO. E. MYERS.

PUBLISHED BY

THOMAS & MATTILL,

265-275 Woodland Avenue, CLEVELAND, OHIO.

PREFACE.

THE LORD'S PRAYER.

E. S. LORENZ.

(2)

RICHES OF GRACE.

1. WINNING SOULS FOR THE MASTER.

E. S. LORENZ.   E. S. LORENZ.

1. We have found a   blest em-ploy, Work that brings suprem-est joy,
2. What tho' tri - als   we must face, What tho' thorn-y paths we trace,
3. For each long-ing souls to win, For each pang o'er oth-ers sin,
4. Gladness here and rapt-ure there O'er the gathered sheaves so fair,

Whose deep peace finds no al - loy,— Winning souls for the Mas - ter.
God still grants a-bounding grace,—Winning souls for the Mas - ter.
Christ more ful- ly reigns with-in, Winning souls for the Mas - ter.
Which we to the gar - ner bear, Winning souls for the Mas - ter.

CHORUS.

Winning souls, winning souls, Bringing them to the bless- ed Mas-ter!

Winning souls,   winning souls, Winning souls for the Mas - ter!

2. DON'T WAIT FOR TO-MORROW.

I. B.

REV. I. BALTZELL.

1. Oh, come to the Sav-ior to-day, 'Tis fol-ly to
2. Oh, look to the cross where he died, And think of his
3. How ma-ny have gone to the grave, Whose end was de-
4. Then fly to the Sav-ior to-day, And walk in the

wait for to-mor-row; Then why will you long-er de-lay?
an-guish and sor-row? Then give up your fol-ly and pride;
struc-tion and hor-ror; Oh, would you have Je-sus to save:
way that is nar-row; 'Twill lead you from fol-ly a-way,

CHORUS.

To-mor-row may fill you with sor-row.
It may be too late on the mor-row.
Then wait not to seek him to-mor-row.
And give you a joy-ous to-mor-row.

The Sav-ior is call-ing to-

day, yes, to-day, Oh, bring him your troub-le and sor-row; Come,

bow at his foot-stool and pray, It may be too late on to-morrow.

3. I'LL BE A SOLDIER.

H. A. HENRY.   CHAS. H. GABRIEL.

1. I'll be a sol-dier, a val-iant sol-dier, too; I will buck-le
2. I'll be a sol-dier, a faith-ful sol-dier, too; I will nev-er
3. I'll be a sol-dier, a loy-al sol-dier, too, Shirk-ing not the

on the ar-mor of the Lord; Firm as a rock I will loy-al be, and true,
turn my back up-on the foe, Watching in prayer, I will ev-er dare to do
duties that are fraught with care; For there's a time coming for a grand re-view,

CHORUS.

Follow-ing the or-ders written in his word.) On - ward! on - ward!
Faithful ser-vice for my Captain here be-low. }
And I want to muster with the faithful there.) Onward, forward! onward, forward!

Not a-fraid to suf-fer pain and loss; Stand-ing for the right, with

vic-to-ry in sight, Yes, I will be a sol-dier of the cross.

NO ROOM IN HEAVEN.

W. O. CUSHING.   I. BALTZELL.

1. How sad it would be, if when thou didst call, All hopeless and
2. How sad it would be, the har-vest all past, The bright summer
3. Oh, haste thee, and fly, while mer-cy is near, Re-member the

un-for-giv-en, The an-gel that stands at the beau-ti-ful gate,
days all o-ver; To know that the reap-ers had gather'd the grain,
love that he gave you; The love that has sought thee is seeking thee still,

CHORUS.

Should an-swer, No room in heav-en.)
And left thee a-lone for-ev-er. } Sad, sad, sad would it be!
And Je-sus now waits to save you.)

No room in heav-en for thee! No room, no room, No room in

Slow and soft.

heaven for thee! No room, no room, No room in heaven for thee!

COME HOME!

H. F. JAMES.

E. S. LORENZ.

1. Ye souls that roam in darkness drear, Come home, come home!
2. Tho' oft refused, the Sav - ior waits, Come home, come home!
3. Your sins tho' great will be for-giv'n, Come home, come home!
4. These pleading tears your heart must melt, Come home, come home!

Come home, come home!

Op-pressed by gloom, by haunt-ing fear, Come home, come home!
Love calls for you at heav-en's gate, Come home, come home!
Here waits for you life, love and heav'n, Come home, come home!
If aught of love your soul has felt, Come home, come home!

Come home, come home!

CHORUS.

Come, come, he is call-ing for thee! Come, come, he is

Call - - ing, call - -

call - ing for thee! Je - sus is call - ing, in sweet ac - cents

ing,

1 2

fall - ing, Is call - ing thee to come, to come! come!

6.
FOR THE MASTER.

J. A. P.   J. A. PARKS.

1. There are vict'ries yet to win, "For the Mas-ter!" We must fight the hosts of
2. There's a cross that you must bear "For the Master!" If a crown of life you'd
3. There are sheaves to gather in "For the Master!" Till the world is saved from

sin "For the Mas - ter!" Sound the watch-word o'er and o'er, Till a -
wear, "For the Mas - ter;" Quick-ly for the fight ar-ray Do not
sin "For the Mas - ter!" Oh! the har-vest fields are white Soon, ah

bove the bat-tle's roar, It shall ring from shore to shore, "For the Mas-ter!"
fal-ter on the way Lest we fail to win the day "For the Mas - ter!"
soon will come the night, Let us la-bor with our might "For the Master!"

CHORUS.

Marching on, We are marching on, while we sing; Marching on, we are

march-ing on, for the King; Sound the watch-word o'er and o'er, Till a -

FOR THE MASTER. Concluded.

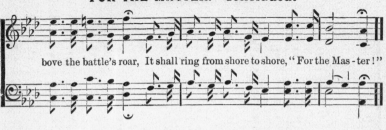

bove the battle's roar, It shall ring from shore to shore, "For the Mas - ter!"

7. WHERE THE SAVIOR LEADS.

JENNIE WILSON.   JOHN TIBBALLS.

1. I would tread that pathway on - ly, Where the lov-ing Sav - ior leads,
2. I will go what-e'er be-falls me, Where the lov-ing Sav - ior leads,
3. Blessings sweet are free - ly giv - en, Where the lov-ing Sav - ior leads,

Tho' the road be bright or lone - ly Where the loving Sav - ior leads.
Ho - ly voic - es soft - ly call me Where the loving Sav - ior leads.
Com-fort, peace and joy from heaven, Where the loving Sav - ior leads.

CHORUS.

Trust-ing him who faileth nev - er, Bound by ties that naught can sever,

Glad-ly will I fol - low ev - er Where the lov-ing Sav-ior leads.

9

8.

HE REDEEMED ME.

GEO. B. MARQUART.

S. C. HANSON.

1. From a roy-al throne that in heav-en shone The kind and loving
2. Oh, be glad and sing, for he came to bring Re-demption to a
3. When on earth he dwelt, oft in prayer he knelt The lost and err-ing
4. He transformed the tomb with its night of gloom,—Let not his children

Sav-ior came, The low-ly to raise and bring to his praise, Who
help-less race: Raise high now each voice, come sing and rejoice—We're
world to save; Oh won-der-ful tho't, with ten-derness fraught, His
cease to sing; The deeds of his love, he pleads now a-bove, Our

CHORUS.

trust in his pre-cious name.
saved by his boun-teous grace.
life for his foes he gave.
Sav-ior and Friend and King.

He redeemed me, he re-

He redeemed me, yes, he

deemed me, From my sin he set me free! He re-
saves a fall-en race,
He re-

deemed me, He redeemed me, He re-deemed me on Cal-va-ry.
deemed me, yes, I am saved by his grace,

9. WONDERFUL LOVE OF JESUS.

E. D. MUND.

E. S. LORENZ.

1. In vain in high and ho - ly lays My soul her grate - ful
2. A joy by day, a peace by night, In storms a calm, in
3 My hope for par - don when I call, My trust for lift - ing

voice would raise; For who can sing the wor - thy praise Of the
dark - ness light; In pain a balm, in weak - ness might, Is the
when I fall; In life, in death, my all in all, Is the

CHORUS.

won - der-ful love of Je - sus! Won - der-ful love!

won - der-ful love! Won - der-ful love of Je - sus!

Won-der-ful love, won-der-ful love! Won-der-ful love of Je - sus!

BLESSED ASSURANCE.

F. J. CROSBY.

MRS. JOSEPH F. KNAPP.

1. Bless- ed as - sur - ance, Je - sus is mine! Oh, what a
2. Per - fect sub - mis - sion, per - fect de - light, Vis - ions of
3. Per - fect sub - mis - sion, all is at rest, I in my

fore - taste of glo - ry di - vine! Heir of sal - va - tion, purchase of
rap - ture now burst on my sight, An-gels de - scend- ing, bring from a -
Sav - iour am hap-py and blest, Watching and wait-ing, look-ing a -

God, Born of his spir - it, wash'd in his blood.)
bove, Ech- oes of mer - cy, whispers of love. } This is my sto - ry,
bove, Fill'd with his goodness, lost in his love.)

this is my song, Praising my Saviour all the day long; This is my

sto - ry, this is my song, Praising my Sav-iour all the day long.

11. ARE YOU READY?

J. W. SLAUGHENHAUPT.

E. S. LORENZ.

1. Soon the   evening shadows fall-ing Close the day of mor-tal life;
2. Soon the   aw-ful trumpet sounding Calls thee to the judgment throne;
3. Oh, how   fa-tal 'tis to lin-ger! Art thou read-y—read-y now?
4. Priceless love and free sal-va-tion Free-ly still are offered thee;

Soon the hand of death ap-pal-ling Draws thee from its wea-ry strife.
Now pre-pare, for love a-bounding Yet has left thee not a-lone.
Read-y, should Death's i-cy fin-ger Lay its chill up-on thy brow?
Yield no long-er to temp-ta-tion, But from sin and sor-row flee.

CHORUS.

Are you read-y?   are you read-y?   'Tis the
Are you ready?   are you ready?

Spir-it call-ing, why de-lay? Are you read-y?
Are you read-y?

are you read-y?   Do not lin-ger long-er, come to-day.
are you ready?

12.
HALLOWED BE HIS NAME.

REV. E. A. HOFFMAN.

J. H. TENNEY.

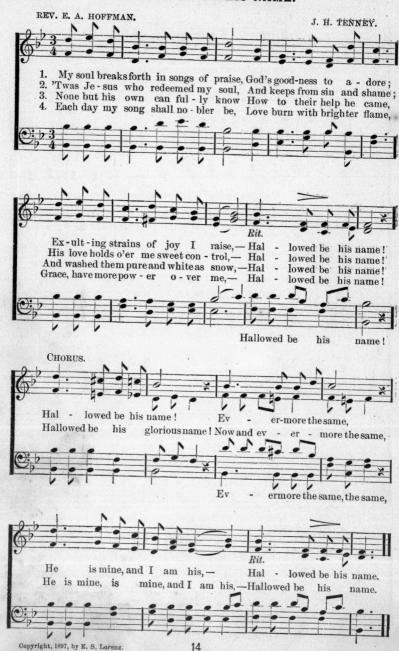

1. My soul breaks forth in songs of praise, God's good-ness to a-dore;
2. 'Twas Je-sus who redeemed my soul, And keeps from sin and shame;
3. None but his own can ful-ly know How to their help he came,
4. Each day my song shall no-bler be, Love burn with brighter flame,

Ex-ult-ing strains of joy I raise,— Hal - lowed be his name!
His love holds o'er me sweet con - trol,— Hal - lowed be his name!
And washed them pure and white as snow,—Hal - lowed be his name!
Grace, have more pow - er o - ver me,— Hal - lowed be his name!

Rit.

Hallowed be his name!

CHORUS.

Hal - lowed be his name! Ev - er-more the same,
Hallowed be his glorious name! Now and ev - er - more the same,

Ev - ermore the same, the same,

Rit.

He is mine, and I am his,— Hal - lowed be his name.
He is mine, is mine, and I am his,—Hallowed be his name.

13.

I AM LISTENING.

W. S. MARSHALL.   W. S. MARSHALL.

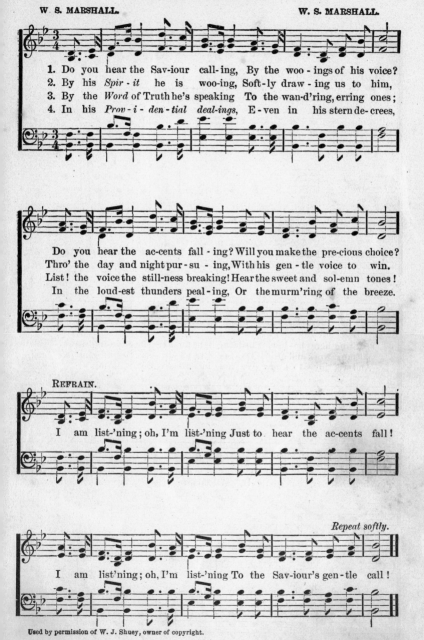

1. Do you hear the Sav-iour call-ing, By the woo-ings of his voice?
2. By his *Spir - it* he is woo-ing, Soft-ly draw-ing us to him,
3. By the *Word* of Truth he's speaking To the wan-d'ring, erring ones;
4. In his *Prov - i - den - tial deal-ings*, E - ven in his stern de-crees,

Do you hear the ac-cents fall - ing? Will you make the pre-cious choice?
Thro' the day and night pur - su - ing, With his gen - tle voice to win.
List! the voice the still-ness breaking! Hear the sweet and sol-emn tones!
In the loud-est thunders peal-ing, Or the murm'ring of the breeze.

REFRAIN.

I am list-'ning; oh, I'm list-'ning Just to hear the ac-cents fall!

Repeat softly.

I am list'ning; oh, I'm list-'ning To the Sav-iour's gen-tle call!

SHINING AS WE GO.

IDA SCOTT TAYLOR.

GEO. E. MEYERS.

1. We are lit-tle jew-els, Brightly we will shine For the crown im-mor-tal Of the King di-vine. 'Tis our sweet-est pleas-ure, Trav'ling here be-low, Shedding light for Je-sus, Shin-ing as we go.
2. We are lit-tle jew-els, Tho' but small, 'tis true, We've a bless-ed mis-sion For our King to do; We've a place ap-point-ed, We must work and grow, Do-ing all for Je-sus, Shin-ing as we go.
3. We are lit-tle jew-els, And our shoulders bear Lit-tle dai-ly cross-es, Lit-tle loads of care; Je-sus helps and guides us, And 'tis joy to know We are in his ser-vice, Shin-ing as we go.

CHORUS.

When the Sav-ior com-eth All his own to claim, Gath'ring up his jew-els, Call-ing them by name— We shall be a-mong them,

SHINING AS WE GO. Concluded.

We shall brightly glow, Scatt'ring rays of sunlight—Shining as we go.

15. FEED MY LAMBS.

JULIA C. ALDRICH.   MARIAN E. OGDEN.

1. Je - sus said with ten - der plead-ing "Feed my lambs, feed my lambs,"
2. Seek each lit - tle son and daughter, "Feed my lambs, feed my lambs,"
3. Tell them of a home in glo - ry, "Feed my lambs, feed my lambs,"

In his word he's in - ter - ced - ing, "Feed my pre - cious lambs."
Lead them to the liv - ing wa - ter, "Feed my pre - cious lambs."
And re - peat the old, old sto - ry To the pre - cious lambs.

REFRAIN.

"Feed my lambs, feed my lambs, If ye love me," saith the Sav - ior,

"Feed my lambs, feed my lambs, If ye love me, feed my lambs."

R. of G. 2 R. N.

16.

KEEP ME CLOSE TO THEE.

LAURA E. NEWELL.

W. A. OGDEN.

1. Tho' he slay me, I will trust him, Christ shall my sal-va-tion be;
2. Hide thy face from me no long-er, Light my pathway with thy love,
3. Tho' my fond-est hopes may perish, And my best en-deav-ors fail;
4. When I cross death's stormy riv-er, Then my soul shall rest in thee,

When he calls me I will an-swer "Yes, O Lord, I come to thee."
Let my faith in thee grow stronger, Till I wor-ship thee a-bove.
Thou wilt keep me till I see thee Safe at last with-in the vale.
In the home of ma-ny mansions, Thou hast there prepared for me.

CHORUS.

Keep me Savior, thine forev-er, Till thy bless-ed face I see,
Keep, oh keep me

Naught from me thy love shall sever, Keep me, Savior, close to thee.
Naught, oh Lord, from

17.
PARDON FOR ALL.

Words adapted.

I. BALTZELL.

1. I once was a stran-ger to grace and to God; I knew not my
2. Then free grace a-woke me by light from on high; I cried, "Je-sus
3. My ter-rors all van-ished be-fore that sweet name; My guilt-y fears
4. Dear Je-sus, dear Je-sus, my treasure and boast; Dear Je-sus, dear

dan-ger, al felt not my load; I flew to the cross when I heard Je-sus
save me, O save, or I die!" He heard my deep pleading, he answered my
banished, with boldness I came To him who had saved from the curse of the
Je-sus, I ne'er can be lost; This watchword shall be my last song when I

REFRAIN. ff

call, "Come, poor, trembling sinner, there is pardon for all."
call; Bless the name of Jesus, there is par-don for all.
fall; Bless the name of Jesus, there is par-don for all.
fall; Bless the name of Jesus, there is par-don for all.

} Par-don for all,

par-don for all; Bless the name of Je-sus, there is par-don for all.

HARVESTERS, GO FORTH.

W. M. W.

W. M. WEEKLEY.

1. The har-vest is great and the fields are all white, And few that will
2. The Mas-ter commands, you should quickly o - bey, To halt in your
3. How few are the moments we're giv - en be - low, How great is the
4. Soon reap-ers of God, with their sick-les in hand, De-scend-ing the

en - ter there-in; How sad is the tho't of the on-com-ing night,
du - ty is sin; The mill-ions are dy - ing O haste you a - way
work for us all; O Lord of the har-vest, thy Spir - it be-stow,
skies we shall see; They'll gath-er the wheat and the tares from all lands,

CHORUS.

When no one can save from sin.
To gath - er the har-vest in.
And help ere the shadows fall.
O what will that har-vest be? } Ye har - vest-ers, go forth to-day,

See whit-'ning fields be - fore you in sin; Im - mor - tals are

per - ish-ing, do not de-lay, O gath - er the har-vest in.

19. ROLLING EVERY BURDEN ON THE LORD.

E. E. HEWITT.   E. S. LORENZ.

1. Close to Je-sus I'll a-bide, Rolling ev-'ry burden on the
2. For the pass-ing need he'll care, Rolling ev-'ry burden on the
3. Well he knows what time will bring, Rolling ev-'ry burden on the
4. O what bless-ing now is mine, Rolling ev-'ry burden on the

Lord, on the Lord; Lin-ger by his bless-ed side, Roll-ing ev-'ry
Lord, on the Lord; Full pro-vis-ion, roy-al fare, Roll-ing ev-'ry
Lord, on the Lord; O-ver all he reign-eth King, Roll-ing ev-'ry
Lord, on the Lord; Par-don, peace, and joy Di-vine! Roll-ing ev-'ry

CHORUS.

bur-den on the Lord!   Rolling ev-'ry burden on the Lord!
           on the Lord! Roll-ing   ev-'ry burden on the Lord!

Rolling ev-'ry bur-den on the Lord! He will us sus-tain,
Roll-ing ev-'ry burden on the Lord! He will us sus-tain,

Give e-ter-nal gain,— Rolling ev'ry burden on the Lord!
Give e-ternal gain,   on the Lord!

20. LET YOUR LIGHT SHINE OUT.

MRS. M. L. HERR.

M. L. McPHAIL.

1. Have you en - tered the race for the prize, my brother, For the
2. Does the path- way seem te - dious and lone, my brother, Are you
3. There are pil- grims who need kind- ly words, my brother, Like our
4. Time for win - ning the prize, is but short, my brother, Then so
5. Then be vig - i - lant, loy - al, and firm, my brother, For the

crown of im - mor - tal life? Do you earn - est - ly run for the
wea - ry, perplexed or faint? Be cour - a - geous, for Christ is at
Lord, let us cheer and bless An - y sea - son, or place we can
run that you may ob - tain; Keep your eyes fixed on Je - sus a -
en - e - my lies in wait, Ev - er wear the whole ar - mor of

D.S.—shad - ows that you may dis-

FINE.   CHORUS.

goal, my brother? Are you fearless a-mid earth's strife?
hand, my brother, To de - liv - er each burdened saint.
serve my brother, Surely makes our own burdens less.
lone my brother, He will make all your pathway plain.
God, my brother, And your vic - to - ry will be great.

} Let your light shine

pel, my broth-er, Je - sus says, "Let your light shine out."

D.S.

out clean and bright, my brother, As you travel thro' darkness and doubt: There are

21. ## THE MATCHLESS NAME.

REV. E. A. HOFFMAN.   J. H. TENNEY.

1. Praise the matchless name of Je - sus,   And a- dore him ev - er-more;
2. My transgressions are for - giv - en,   Ban- ished to a land unknown;
3. O   this wondrous, wondrous Savior !   O   the triumphs of his grace !
4. Let me ev - er-more con-fess him   For his good-ness un - to me;

He has wrought redemption for me,—   Tell the sto - ry   o'er and o'er.
Writ- ten now my name in heav - en,   Heir to an im - mor-tal crown.
O   the sweetness of his fa - vor!   O   his love to   all the race.
Let me praise and let me bless him   Here and in e - ter - ni - ty.

mp CHORUS.

Then grate-ful - ly a -dore him, O lov-ing- ly a -dore him; And
name, O then a -dore him,

1   *f*

of - fer now be- fore him Praise to his matchless name,   Then
                                    name, to his matchless

2

of - fer now be - fore him Praise to his match - less name.

22. A FRIEND IN JESUS.

IDA SCOTT TAYLOR.   E. S. LORENZ.

1. It is sweet to have a friend in Je - sus, As we jour-ney here be-low;
2. It is sweet to have a friend in Je - sus, Who is always strong and true;
3. It is sweet to have a friend in Je - sus, As the fleet-ing years go by;
4. It is sweet to have a friend in Je - sus, For his love no change can know;

For no mat-ter what we do   He will lead us safe-ly thro',—It is
Ev - 'ry bur-den he will bear, Ev - 'ry sor-row he will share,—It is
On his strength we may de-pend, He will keep us to the end,—It is
Tho' we sometimes careless roam, He will gen-tly lead us home,—It is

CHORUS.

It is sweet . . . . . . to have a

sweet to have a friend in Je - sus. It is sweet to have a friend, Such a

friend,   Such a lov - - - ing, ten - der

lov - ing, ten - der friend; It is sweet to have a friend, Such a

friend,

lov - ing, ten - der friend! For no mat - ter what we do He will

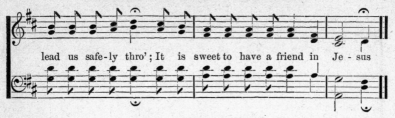

lead us safe-ly thro'; It is sweet to have a friend in Je - sus

23.

KEEP ME THIS DAY.

FANNY J. CROSBY.   ADAM GEIBEL.

SOLO OR QUARTET.

1. Keep me, O Lord, this day O keep thou me, Beneath thy care and
2. Keep me, O Lord, this day from ev-'ry sin, Close thou my heart, nor
3. Keep me, O Lord, this day, and may I feel The ho - ly joy thy

sheltered close to thee; Keep me this day, my erring footsteps guide, That
let the tempter in; Keep me this day, o - be-dient to thy will, And
precious words re - veal; Keep me this day, as all my life be - fore, Keep

CHORUS.

from the right I may not turn a - side. }
with thy love my long-ing spir - it fill. } Keep me, O Lord, this
thou my heart, O Lord, I ask no more. }

day, O keep thou me, That I may dwell in per-fect peace with thee.

WALKING IN THE LIGHT.

EDEN READE LATTA.

W. A. OGDEN.

1. Are you walk-ing in the light, That is shining clear and bright, On the
2. Are you walk-ing in the light, That will guide your feet a-right, Tho' the
3. Are you walk-ing in the light, Trusting in the Savior's might, Are you

path that leads to heav'n and God? Are you keep-ing, day by day, In the
sky may be with clouds o'ercast? Are you keep-ing still in view, What is
lean-ing on his prom-ise blest? If but faith-ful you will be, Till shall

ev-er-last-ing way, Where the pil-grims, gone be-fore you have trod?
prom-ised un-to you, If you pa-tient-ly en-dure to the last?
dawn e-ter-ni-ty, You shall en-ter in-to glo-ri-ous rest!

CHORUS.

Are you walk - - ing in the light, ...
walk-ing in the light, walk-ing in the light,

In your age, or in your youth? Are you walk - - ing
walk-ing in the light,

WALKING IN THE LIGHT. Concluded.

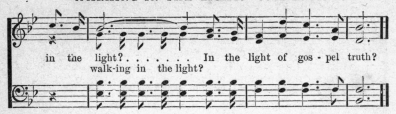

in the light?...... In the light of gos - pel truth?
walk-ing in the light?

25. HELP OTHERS.

HARRIET E. JONES. CHAS. K. LANGLEY.

1. There are break-ing hearts to - day, That may sing to - mor - row,
2. Out from thy God - giv - en store, Some one be re - liev - ing;
3. Im - i - tate the Sav - ior kind, Help your suff-'ring broth - ers;

If you strive in lov - ing way, To as - suage their sor - row.
Bless-ed, he, who helps the poor— Smile of God re - ceiv - ing.
Tru - est pleas - ure you may find In your work for oth - ers.

CHORUS.

Plant some ros - es in the path Of your suff-'ring broth - ers!

Prove your near-ness to the Christ, By your work for oth - ers.

SHINE WHERE YOU ARE.

JESSIE H. BROWN.   E. S. LORENZ.

1. Would you have the world bet - ter and brighter? Then light up the
2. Make the world that you live in your debt-or, As thro' it you
3. Trim the lamp that is left to your keep-ing, And fan it with

way as you go; Make some lit - tle part of it light-er
jour - ney a - long; Be good, and the earth will grow bet - ter,
breez - es of hope; Lest shad - ows your life o - ver-creep-ing,

CHORUS.

With beams from your life's stead- y glow. }   Then shine where you are and the
Do right, and the right will grow strong. } { Yes, shine where you are and life's
Leave oth - ers in dark-ness to grope. }

world will be the bright-er! } You'll bright en, my broth - er, the
bur - dens will be light - er! }

path of an - oth - er, And life will be bright - er for you.

27.

LOVING DEEDS.

G. E. M.

GEO. E. MYERS.

1. Let us do a deed of kind-ness ev-'ry day, Let us
2. Let us seek the priv-i-lege of deeds of love, Striv-ing
3. Let us help each oth-er war a-gainst the wrong, Strengthen

light-en cares and bur-dens on the way; Let us help to raise the
thus to hon-or Him who dwells a-bove; Searching out the suff'ring,
one an-oth-er with in-spir-ing song; Let us trust in God and

D.S.—*Scat-ter lov-ing words a-*

fal-len and oppressed, Let us tell them of the Savior's prom-ised rest.
help-less and distressed, Let us fill their lives with hope and promise blest.
read his bless-ed word, Let us fol-low our Ex-am-ple, Christ the Lord.

long the paths we tread, Lend a help-ing hand to all who are in need.

CHORUS.

Let us help each oth-er on, in the bat-tle to be won,

D.S.

Let us ban-ish ev-'ry sel-fish thought and deed;

29

CHRIST AT THE HELM.

J. H. A.

J. H. ALLEMAN.

1. Now as on life's sea I glide, In my frag-ile bark un-tried, I will
2. Mur-mur not tho' tri-als sore, Strew thy pathway all be-fore, But re-
3. He who uttered "Peace be still," Calmed the angry waves at will, Guides us

fear not tho' angry waves o'erwhelm; Dim-ly thro' the storm of night I be-
mem-ber what he hath done for thee; Christ, the mighty one to save, Rose a
on-ward to yon-der bet-ter realm; Haste your courage to re-new, Soon the

hold the har-bor light; Cheer up, com-rades, for Christ is at the helm.
vic-tor o'er the grave; He will ev - er our faith-ful pi - lot be.
har-bor we shall view; Cheer up, com-rades, for Christ is at the helm.

CHORUS.

Hal - le - lu - jah! Hal - le - lu - jah! Naught can my frail bark o'erwhelm;

Hal - le - lu - jah! Hal - le - lu - jah! Christ is standing at the helm.

29. TELL IT TO JESUS.

J. E. RANKIN, D.D.   E. S. LORENZ.

1. Are you wea - ry, are you heav-y-heart-ed? Tell it to Je - sus,
2. Do the tears flow down your cheeks unbidden? Tell it to Je - sus,
3. Do you fear the gath'ring clouds of sor - row? Tell it to Je - sus,
4. Are you troub-led with the thought of dying? Tell it to Je - sus,

Tell it to Je - sus. Are you griev-ing o - ver joys de-part-ed?
Tell it to Je - sus. Have you sins that to man's eye are hid-den?
Tell it to Je - sus. Are you anx-ious what shall be to-mor-row?
Tell it to Je - sus. For Christ's com-ing Kingdom are you sigh-ing?

CHORUS.

Tell it to Je - sus a - lone. Tell it to Je - sus, Tell it to

Je - sus, He is a friend that's well known: You have no oth - er

such a friend or broth - er? Tell it to Je - sus a - lone.

30.

THE KING COMES IN.

ADA BLENKHORN.   CHAS. H. GABRIEL.

1. Our hearts will sing with glad-ness, When the King .... comes in ;
2. With joy-ful hearts we'll meet him, When the King .... comes in ;
3. O sweet and won-drous sto-ry, When the King .... comes in ;

When the King

We'll bid fare-well to sad-ness, When the King . . . comes in.
With songs of welcome greet him, When the King .... comes in.
Our eyes shall see his glo-ry, When the King .... comes in.

When the King

No room for care or sor-row, Each hap-py, bright to-mor-row
The joy-bells all a-ring-ing, Our hal-le-lu-jahs sing-ing,
What transport! him be-hold-ing, His arms a-round us fold-ing,

From him its light will bor-row, When the King .... comes in.
All glo-ry to him bring-ing, When the King .... comes in.
Our rap-tured souls up-hold-ing, When the King .... comes in.

When the King

CHORUS.

When the King . . . . . comes in, ... When the
When the King, when the King of glo-ry comes in, When the

THE KING COMES IN. Concluded.

King . . . . comes in, ... We shall then be-
King, when the King of glo-ry comes in,

hold his glo-ry, When the King . . . . comes in . . . .
When the King comes in.

31. JESUS LOVES THE CHILDREN.

ROBERT LOWE FLETCHER.   W. A. OGDEN.

1. Je-sus loves the chil-dren, Bids them ear-ly come; He would have them
2. In his arms he folds them Like a shepherd true; By his Spir-it
3. Je-sus glad-ly welcomes Those who seek his face, Lov-ing-ly re-
4. Je-sus is our Sav-ior; We would love him more, Be his faith-ful

CHORUS.

nev-er From his paths to roam.
leads them In-to pas-tures new.   } Je-sus, pre-cious Je-sus, Leads us
ceives them In his kind em-brace.
chil-dren, And his name a-dore.

all the way; We would ear-ly seek thee, And thy call o-bey.

       R. of G. 3 R. N.

32. O, WHAT A SAVIOR.

H. F. JAMES.

E. S. LORENZ.

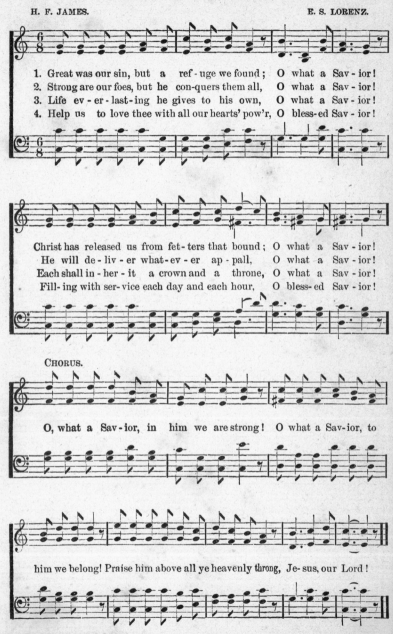

1. Great was our sin, but a ref - uge we found; O what a Sav - ior!
2. Strong are our foes, but he con-quers them all, O what a Sav - ior!
3. Life ev - er - last-ing he gives to his own, O what a Sav - ior!
4. Help us to love thee with all our hearts' pow'r, O bless-ed Sav - ior!

Christ has released us from fet-ters that bound; O what a Sav - ior!
He will de - liv - er what-ev - er ap - pall, O what a Sav - ior!
Each shall in - her - it a crown and a throne, O what a Sav - ior!
Fill- ing with ser- vice each day and each hour, O bless- ed Sav - ior!

CHORUS.

O, what a Sav - ior, in him we are strong! O what a Sav - ior, to

him we belong! Praise him above all ye heavenly throng, Je- sus, our Lord!

34

TRUST HIM MORE.

W. A. O.

W. A. OGDEN.

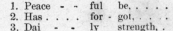

1. Peace - - ful be, ...
2. Has . . . . for - got, ...
3. Dai - - ly strength, .

1. Since thy Fa-ther's arm sustains thee, Peaceful be, peace-ful be;
2. Fear - est sometime that thy Fa-ther Has for - got? has for - got?
3. To his own thy Sav - ior giv - eth Dai - ly strength, dai - ly strength,

It . . . . is he, . . .
Doubt . . him not, . . .
Peace . . at length, .

When a chast'ning hand restrains thee, It is he, it is he.
When the clouds a - round thee gath-er, Doubt him not, doubt him not.
To each troubled soul that liv - eth, Peace at length, peace at length.

Know his love in full completeness Is the measure of thy weakness;
Al- ways hath the day - light broken, Al - ways he hath com-fort spo- ken;
Weak-est lambs have larg-est shar-ing Of this ten-der Shepherd's car-ing;

Trust . . him more. . .
Than . . thy fears. . .
On - - ly bow . .

Rit.

If he wound thy spir - it sore, Trust him more, trust him more.
Bet - ter hath he been for years Than thy fears, than thy fears.
Ask him not, then, where or how, On - ly bow, on - ly bow.

34. WHEN THOU HAST SHUT THY DOOR.

E. E. HEWITT.   ADAM GEIBEL.

1. Come near to thy Fa-ther and tell him thy need, When
2. He "seeth in se-cret," he knows all thy grief, When
3. Though low at the cross falls the pen-i-tent tear, When
4. There drink-ing so free-ly from heav-en-ly springs, When

thou . . . . hast shut thy door; His
thou . . . . hast shut thy door; His
thou . . . . hast shut thy door, His
thou . . . . . . hast shut thy door, Re-
thou hast shut thy door, When thou hast shut thy door;

love and his mer-cy, his prom-is-es plead, When thou . . . . hast
com-fort-ing Spir-it will bring thee re-lief, When thou . . . . hast
read-y for-giveness will bring thee good cheer, When thou . . . . hast
newed, day by day, thou shalt find eagle wings, When thou . . . . hast
thou hast shut thy door,

CHORUS.

shut thy door. . . . . .
shut thy door. . . . . . .
shut thy door. . . . . . .   } Close on the world the door of thy heart,
shut thy door. . . . . . .
When thou hast shut thy door.

WHEN THOU HAST SHUT THY DOOR. Concluded.

Turn from its cares, its pleasures a-part; Thy Fa-ther will bless thee wher-

ev - er thou art, When thou . . . . hast shut thy door.
thou hast shut thy door, When thou hast shut thy door.

35. THOU WILT NOT LEAVE ME.

E. E. HEWITT.
DUET.

E. S. LORENZ.

1. Sav - ior, my life, my all, Thou wilt not leave me; Read - y to
2. Tho' other friends should fail, Thou wilt not leave me; Grace shall "much
3. Joy com - eth from the throne, Thou wilt not leave me; Wand'ring no

hear my call, Thou wilt not leave me. Thy lov - ing voice I heard,
more" pre-vail, Thou wilt not leave me. "Thou hast a might - y arm,"
more a - lone, Thou wilt not leave me. O, may I rest in thee,

This precious promised word, Sweetly my heart it stirred, Thou wilt not leave me.
Shielding my soul from harm; Hush thou each wild alarm, Thou wilt not leave me.
Trust - ful, o - be-dient be, Then, Lord, thy face I'll see, Thou wilt not leave me.

36.

THERE IS JOY.

REV. F. L. SNYDER.

GEO. E. MYERS.

1. Have you found in trust-ing God There is joy, there is joy? In the
2. Have you felt that in your heart There is joy, there is joy? When you
3. Have you found in do-ing good There is joy, there is joy? When you
4. Have you heard that up in heaven There is joy, there is joy? When a

way our father's trod There is joy, there is joy. When you try to do the
al-ways do your part There is joy, there is joy. When you al-ways sing and
live just as you should There is joy, there is joy. When you help the struggling
soul on earth's forgiv'n There is joy, there is joy. There is joy both here and

right When you're living in the light When you walk by faith, not sight, There is joy.
pray. When you have a word to say For your Sav-ior ev-'ry day, There is joy.
weak, When you words of kindness speak And the good of others seek, There is joy.
there, In its bliss we all may share; Till at last a crown we wear There is joy.

CHORUS.

There is joy, there is joy, There is joy, there is joy, In the ser-vice of the

Lord There is joy, there is joy; When we walk the nar-row way, When we

THERE IS JOY. Concluded.

la-bor, sing and pray, And the Sav-ior we o-bey, There is joy, there is joy.

37. ## THE SWEETEST LESSON.

R. H. BUTLER.

1. Sav - ior, teach me, day by day, Love's sweet les-son to o - bey:
2. With a child-like heart of love, At thy bid-ding may I move;
3. Love in lov - ing finds em-ploy— In o - be-dience all her joy;

Sweet-er les - son can not be— Lov-ing him who first loved me.
Prompt to serve and fol - low thee— Lov-ing him who first loved me.
Ev - er new that joy will be— Lov-ing him who first loved me.

CHORUS.

Lov-ing him . . . who first loved me,   Lov-ing him . . . . who
Lov-ing him   who first loved me,   Loving him

first loved me! Sweeter les - son can not be,—Loving him who first loved me.

38.   IN THE PROMISED LAND.

IDA SCOTT TAYLOR.

E. S. LORENZ.

1. I've a gold-en crown in the Prom-ised Land, In the Prom-ised
2. I've a pure white robe that I long to wear In the Prom-ised
3. Oh, we'll all go home in the by and by To the Prom-ised

Land, in the Promised Land; Where the saints and an-gels prais-ing stand
Land, in the Promised Land; I've an heav'n-ly man-sion bright and fair
Land, to the Promised Land; And we'll dwell be-neath the star-ry sky

CHORUS.

In the glo-rious Prom-ised Land. Oh, hal-le-lu-jah! for I

soon shall be With the saints at rest in those man-sions blest; I'll

walk with saints be-side the crys-tal sea, In the glo-rious Promised Land.

39.   INTO THY KINGDOM.

IDA L. REED.

M. L. MCPHAIL.

1. In - to thy kingdom of peace and love, Sav-ior, the chil-dren come;
2. Out of the highways and paths of sin, In - to thine arms so blest,
3. In - to thy kingdom, O Lamb of God, Guide thou the lit - tle feet;

In - to the realm of thy joy a - bove, In - to thy heav'nly home.
Come the dear children, so sweet and pure, Seeking thy promised rest.
Lest they may wander from thee a - far, Grant them thy mer-cy sweet.

CHORUS.

In - to thy kingdom of joy and light, Out of all lands they come;

Bless-ed are they in thy ho - ly sight, Thy lit - tle ones gath'ring home.

40. RIGHT AT LAST.

REV. JOHNSON OATMAN, JR.

GEO. E. MYERS.

1. O pil-grim on life's pathway here, Tho' oft you are down-cast,
2. Tho' hard with toil has been your lot, Tho' griefs came thick and fast,—
3. Tho' loved ones have gone o'er the tide, And thro' death's portals passed,—

Come, list-en to these words of cheer, 'Twill all be right at last.
When cares of earth are all for-got, 'Twill all be right at last.
You'll meet them on the oth-er side, 'Twill all be right at last.

Tho' clouds are hanging o'er your way, Tho' doubt and fear your soul dis-may,
You may not thro' the dark glass see You won-der why these things must be,—
Your Lord in love goes to pre-pare A king-ly man-sion o-ver there;

Keep toil-ing on till close of day, 'Twill all be right at last.
But when you reach e-ter-ni-ty, 'Twill all be right at last.
You'll find when dawns that morning fair 'Twill all be right at last.

CHORUS.

'Twill all be right at last (at last) When cares of life are past, (are past,)

RIGHT AT LAST. Concluded.

God's word is sure: if we en-dure, 'Twill all be right at last.

41. GOING HOME AT LAST.

REV. W. GOSSETT.

E. S. LORENZ.

1. The eve-ning shades are fall-ing, Our sun is sink-ing fast;
2. The road's been long and drear-y, The toils came thick and fast;
3. We now are near-ing heav-en, And soon shall be at rest;
4. Oh, praise the Lord for-ev-er! Our sor-rows are all past;

The Ho-ly One is call-ing, We're go-ing home at last.
In bo-dy weak and wea-ry, We're go-ing home at last.
Our crowns will soon be giv-en, We're go-ing home at last.
We'll part no more, no nev-er, We are at home at last.

CHORUS.

Go-ing home at last! Go-ing home at last! The

march will soon be o-ver; We're go-ing home at last.

42. SUNSHINE IN THE HEART.

ADAM CRAIG.   CHAS. H. GABRIEL.

1. I've found a balm for ev-'ry woe, That bids my fears de-part!
2. Speak kind-ly to the lit-tle ones, Don't let them drift a-part;
3. Be help-ful to the a-ged ones, Who oft-en sit a-part,

I'm hap-py now since Je-sus sheds His sunshine in my heart.
The Sav-ior loves them and he's shed His sunshine in their heart.
And ask the bless-ed Lord to shed His sunshine in their heart.

CHORUS.

Sun-shine! sun-shine! Let it in your heart! Sun-shine! sun-shine!

Drive the clouds a-part! Je-sus smiles a-bove you,

Bids your cares depart; Ask him, and he'll give you Sunshine in your heart.

4 When earthly friends are called away,
  How sorrow's tears will start;
  The Lord has triumphed over death,
  Let sunshine in your heart.

5 To those who've wander'd far from God,
  Your Savior's love impart;
  Your life will shine, your face will glow,
  He's sunshine in your heart.

43.

FEAR NOT.

VIOLA B. HALL.

E. S. LORENZ.

1. March right for-ward, lit-tle Chris-tian bands; Fear not! oh,
2. Fol-low Christ your lead-er to the end; Fear not! oh,
3. Ear-ly called to bat-tle for the Lord; Fear not! oh,
4. Ev-'ry bat-tle brings you add-ed pow'r; Fear not! oh,

fear not! God will give the bat-tle to your hands;
fear not! He will guide you, ev-er will de-fend;
fear not! Strug-gle brave-ly, trust-ing in his word;
fear not! Grow then grand-ly, ev-'ry day and hour!

CHORUS.

Fear not! oh, fear not! What tho' fierce and long the

strife is rag-ing, God is on your side, the foe en-gag-ing;

Ev-'ry wound he heals, the pain as-suag-ing; Fear not! oh, fear not!

45

44.

GLORY, LAUD, AND HONOR.

PROCESSIONAL HYMN.

REV. J. M. NEALE.

ADAM GEIBEL.

INTRODUCTION.

{ All glo - ry, laud, and hon - or, To thee, Re-deem-er King! }
{ To whom the lips of chil - dren, Made sweet hosan-nas ring. }

Unison.

1. Thou art the King of Is - rael, Thou Da-vid's Roy - al Son,
2. The com - pa - ny of an - gels Are prais-ing thee on high;
3. The peo - ple of the He - brews With palms be - fore thee went:
4. To Thee be - fore thy pas - sion They sang their hymns of praise:
5. Thou did'st ac - cept their prais - es; Ac - cept the prayers we bring,

Who in the Lord's name com - est, The King and Bless-ed One.
And mor-tal men and all things Cre - a - ted, make re - ply.
Our praise and prayer and an - thems Be - fore thee we pre - sent.
To thee, now high ex - alt - ed Our mel - o - dy we raise.
Who in all good de - light - est, Thou good and gra-cious King.

REFRAIN. (*harmony.*)

All glo - ry, laud and hon - or, To thee, Re-deem-er, King! To

GLORY, LAUD, AND HONOR. Concluded.

D.S.

whom the lips of   chil - dren, Made sweet ho-san-nas ring.   A - MEN.

45.   ANSWER HIM, LORD, I WILL.

JENNIE WILSON.

E. S. LORENZ.

1. Je-sus is call-ing you to the light, Sweetly his ac-cents thrill;
2. Je-sus is bidding you at his feet All of your sins to lay;
3. Je-sus invites you to come in faith, La-den with grief and blame;
4. Bid all your hindering doubts depart, Cling to Christ's promise still;

While he is bidding you come to-night, On-ly say, Lord, I will.
He will give pardon and peace complete, Taking your guilt a - way.
I will for-give you, his dear voice saith, Trust in his sav-ing name.
While he is say-ing, give me thine heart, Answer him, Lord, I will.

CHORUS.

On - ly say, Lord, I will, I will! On-ly say, Lord, I will, I will!

While he so ten-der-ly bids you come   Answer him, Lord, I will!

46. A FRIEND, A SONG, A HOME.

IDA SCOTT TAYLOR.

W. A. OGDEN.

1. There's a *Friend* un-chang-ing, true, Je - sus is his name!
2. There's a *Song* I love to sing, Je - sus is its theme!
3. There's a *Home* be - yond the skies, Je - sus is its light!

He has died for love of you; Je - sus is his name!
To my soul it joy doth bring; Je - sus is its theme!
There the soul for ref - uge flies; Je - sus is its light!

Name a - bove all oth - ers dear, How it thrills my list'ning ear,
Oh, the bless - ed, ho - ly song, How it bears my soul a - long,
Light that's fair - er than the day, Where no shad - ows ev - er stray,

Name my soul de-lights to hear, Pre - cious, pre-cious Name!
Theme of rap - ture pure and strong, Pre - cious, pre-cious Song!
Light that nev - er fades a - way, Pre - cious, pre-cious Light!

D.S.—*Make my spir - it more like thine, Je - sus, bless - ed Lord!*

CHORUS.

Je - sus, bless - ed Je - sus mine, Thou art life and light di - vine,

Copyright, 1897, by E. S. Lorenz.

48.

47. 'TIS FREE!

HARRIET E. JONES.　　　　　　　　　　　　　　CHAS. H. GABRIEL.

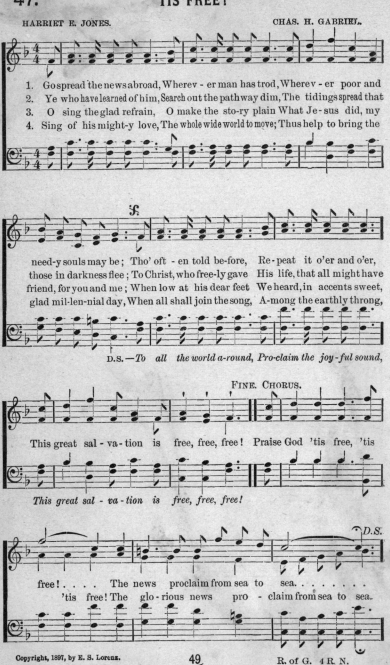

1. Go spread the news abroad, Wherev - er man has trod, Wherev - er poor and
2. Ye who have learned of him, Search out the pathway dim, The tidings spread that
3. O sing the glad refrain, O make the sto-ry plain What Je-sus did, my
4. Sing of his might-y love, The whole wide world to move; Thus help to bring the

need-y souls may be; Tho' oft - en told be-fore, Re - peat it o'er and o'er,
those in darkness flee; To Christ, who free-ly gave His life, that all might have
friend, for you and me; When low at his dear feet We heard, in accents sweet,
glad mil-len-nial day, When all shall join the song, A-mong the earthly throng,

D.S.—*To all the world a-round, Pro-claim the joy-ful sound,*

FINE. CHORUS.

This great sal - va - tion is free, free, free! Praise God 'tis free, 'tis

This great sal - va - tion is free, free, free!

D.S.

free!.... The news proclaim from sea to sea........
'tis free! The glo-rious news pro - claim from sea to sea.

　　　　　　　　　　　R. of G. 4 R. N.

48. HE WONDROUSLY SAVES TO-DAY.

J. H. A.

J. H. ALLEMAN.

1. O for a thousand tongues to sing, He wondrously saves to-day;
2. My gra-cious Mas-ter and my God, He wondrously saves to-day;
3. Je-sus the name that charms our fears, He wondrously saves to-day;
4. He breaks the pow'r of cancelled sin, He wondrously saves to-day;

The glo-ries of my God and King, Who wondrously saves to-day.
Pro-claim thro' all the world abroad, He wondrously saves to-day.
'Tis mu-sic in the sin-ner's ears, He wondrously saves to-day.
His blood can make the foul-est clean, He wondrously saves to-day.

CHORUS.

Sing glo-ry to Je-sus, Who taketh my sins a-way;
Sing glo-ry to Je-sus, sing glo-ry to Je-sus, Who taketh my sins away, away;

Sing glo-ry to Je-sus, Who wondrously saves to-day.
Sing glo-ry to Je-sus, sing glo-ry to Jesus, Who wondrously saves to-day.

5 He speaks, then list ye to his voice,
  He wondrously saves to-day;
Ye mournful, broken hearts rejoice,
  He wondrously saves to-day.

6 Hear him ye deaf, sing praise ye dumb,
  He wondrously saves to-day;
Ye blind behold your Savior come,
  He wondrously saves to-day.

49. WE'LL NEVER SAY GOOD-BYE.

ANNA CHICHESTER.　　　　　　　　　　　　　　E. S. LORENZ.

1. We shall meet ne'er to sev - er　On the banks of the riv - er, Where the
2. As in peace they are sleeping, O'er their graves we are weeping, Love its
3. No more hours, dark, ap-pall-ing, When our friends death is calling, And, while

saints praise for-ev - er　God on high;　　　All our friends we shall
sad vig - il keep-ing Where they lie;　　　Let this hope then be
tears fast are fall-ing, They re - ply;　　　Soon be- yond heav-en's
　　　　　　　　　　　　　God on high;

meet then And with gladness shall greet then, For we'll never say good-bye.
cheering, That the glad hour is nearing When we'll never say good - bye.
por-tals, We shall greet them, immortals, And we'll never say good - bye.

REFRAIN. *1st. time f, 2d time p.*

For we'll nev - er　say good-bye! For we'll nev - er　say good-bye!
When we'll nev - er　say good-bye! When we'll nev-er　say good-bye!
And we'll nev - er　say good-bye! And we'll nev-er　say good-bye!

rit.

Oh! what joy 'twill be to greet them, Where we'll never say good-bye.

51

THE LIGHT OF THE CROSS.

MRS. E. W. CHAPMAN.   J. H. TENNEY.

1. There's a light that is shin-ing to-day,
2. Come, ye chil-dren, be-hold this grand light,
3. Down the mountain it flash-eth a ray,

'Tis the light of the cross,
'Tis the light

'tis the light of the cross; It will guide you a-long the right way,
It will shine thro' the shades of the night,
of the cross; It will drive gloom and dark-ness a-way,

'Tis the light, 'tis the light of the cross.

CHORUS.

'Tis the light of the cross, 'Tis the light of the cross. Light of the cross on

'Tis the light, 'tis the light of the cross.

Cal-va-ry's height, Point-ing to realms of the blest Be the light of my

of the blest,

life, ev-er shin-ing so bright, Guiding me to the ha-ven of rest.

The haven of rest.

51. A BRIGHT NEW HOPE.

E. E. HEWITT.

HOWARD E. SMITH.

1. There's a bright new hope in my heart to-day, There's a light that's
2. There's a bless-ed work I may dai-ly do, As the Mas-ter's
3. There's a sweet new hope in my heart to-day, By the side of

spark-ling up-on my way; For I've come to Je-sus, I've found in him
call-ing I now pur-sue; I must give the mes-sage of wondrous love,
Je-sus, I'll glad-ly stay; He will help me stand when temptations come,

CHORUS.

Bless-ed rays of sunshine that ne'er grow dim. }
I must show the bea-con that burns a-bove.   } A sweet new hope and a
He will lead me on to his glo-rious home.   }

heav'n-ly peace, For Je-sus has sought and found me; Yes, a joy un-

told more precious far than gold, For my Sav-ior's arms are 'round me.

53

52.

EVER FORWARD.

E. S. LORENZ.

GEO. E. MYERS.

Slowly, with strong accent.

1. Fear-ing no e - vil, but trust - ing him who rules a - bove,
2. Bit - ter the rage of the foe who hot - ly doth pur - sue,
3. What tho' the mountains and sea our on - ward march would stay,
4. Vic - to-ries past spur us on new vic - to - ries to win!

For - ward, for - ward we go! God is our lead - er, his
For - ward, for - ward we go! God of the fire and the
For - ward, for - ward we go! Vain their re - sist - ance, the
For - ward, for - ward we go! Joy- ing in con - flict till

Ev- er forward!

ban - ner o - ver us is love; Ev - er for-ward! for-ward we go.
cloud will bring us safe - ly thro'; Ev - er for-ward! for-ward we go.
pow'r of God they but dis-play; Ev - er for-ward! for-ward we go.
heav'nly peace we en - ter in, Ev - er for-ward! for-ward we go.

CHORUS.

For - ward! hear the trum- pet to the glo - ri-ous vic-t'ry call us,
For - ward! ev - er for - ward for no harm can ev - er be- fall us,

EVER FORWARD. Concluded.

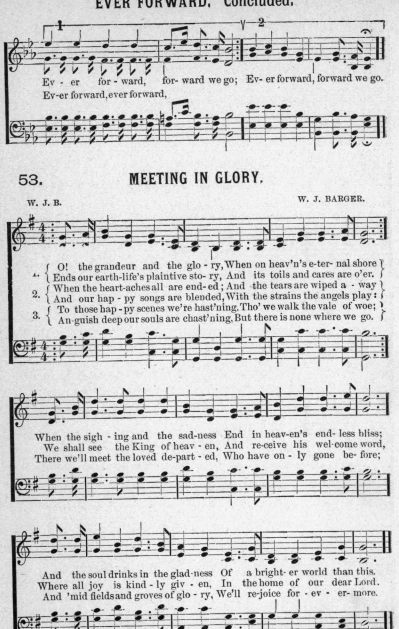

Ev - er   for - ward,   for - ward we go; Ev- er forward, forward we go.
Ev-er forward, ever forward,

53.   **MEETING IN GLORY.**

W. J. B.   W. J. BARGER.

1. { O! the grandeur and the glo - ry, When on heav'n's e-ter- nal shore }
   { Ends our earth-life's plaintive sto - ry, And its toils and cares are o'er. }

2. { When the heart-aches all are end- ed ; And the tears are wiped a - way }
   { And our hap - py songs are blended, With the strains the angels play : }

3. { To those hap - py scenes we're hast'ning, Tho' we walk the vale of woe; }
   { An-guish deep our souls are chast'ning, But there is none where we go. }

When the sigh - ing and the sad-ness End in heav-en's end- less bliss;
We shall see the King of heav - en, And re-ceive his wel-come word,
There we'll meet the loved de-part - ed, Who have on - ly gone be- fore;

And the soul drinks in the glad-ness Of a bright-er world than this.
Where all joy is kind - ly giv - en, In the home of our dear Lord.
And 'mid fields and groves of glo - ry, We'll re-joice for - ev - er- more;

Copyright, 1897, by E. S. Lorenz.

54.

GLORIOUS SUNSHINE.

ADAM CRAIG.

CHAS. H. GABRIEL.

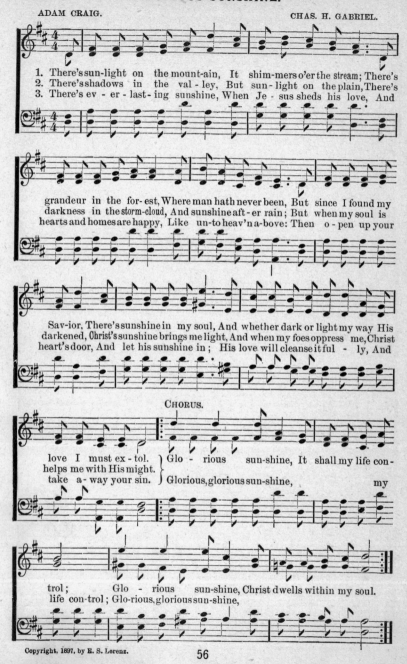

1. There's sun-light on the mount-ain, It shim-mers o'er the stream; There's
2. There's shadows in the val-ley, But sun-light on the plain, There's
3. There's ev-er-last-ing sunshine, When Je-sus sheds his love, And

grandeur in the for-est, Where man hath never been, But since I found my
darkness in the storm-cloud, And sunshine aft-er rain; But when my soul is
hearts and homes are happy, Like un-to heav'n a-bove: Then o-pen up your

Sav-ior, There's sunshine in my soul, And whether dark or light my way His
darkened, Christ's sunshine brings me light, And when my foes oppress me, Christ
heart's door, And let his sunshine in; His love will cleanse it ful-ly, And

CHORUS.

love I must ex-tol. } Glo-rious sun-shine, It shall my life con-
helps me with His might.
take a-way your sin.   } Glorious, glorious sun-shine,   my

trol;   Glo-rious   sun-shine, Christ dwells within my soul.
life con-trol; Glo-rious, glorious sun-shine,

WHEN THE KING COMES IN.

J. E. LANDOR.   E. S. LORENZ.

1. Called to the feast by the King are we, Sit-ting, perhaps, where his
2. Crowns on the head where the thorns have been, Glo - ri - fied he who once
3. Like lightning's flash will that in-stant show Things hidden long from both
4. Joy - ful his eye shall on each one rest Who is in white wedding

peo - ple be, How will it fare, friend, with thee and me
died for men, Splen - did the vis - ion be - fore us then,
friend and foe, Just what we are will each neigh - bor know,
gar - ments dressed, Ah well for us if we stand the test,

REFRAIN.

When the King comes in?
When the King comes in.   } When the King comes in, brother, When the King comes
When the King comes in.
When the King comes in.

in! How will it fare with thee and me When the King comes in?

5 Endless the separation then,
   Bitter the cry of deluded men,
   Awful that moment beyond all ken,
   When the King comes in.

6 Lord, grant us all, we implore thee, grace,
   So to await thee each in his place,
   That we may fear not to see thy face
   When thou comest in.

MORE AND MORE.

G. M. BILLS.

M. L. McPHAIL.

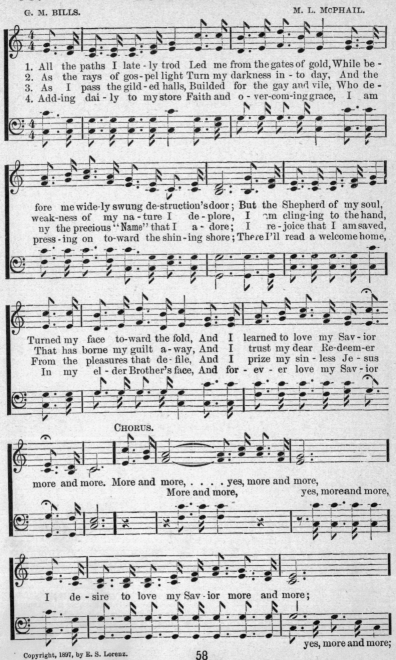

1. All the paths I late-ly trod Led me from the gates of gold, While be-
2. As the rays of gos-pel light Turn my darkness in-to day, And the
3. As I pass the gild-ed halls, Builded for the gay and vile, Who de-
4. Add-ing dai-ly to my store Faith and o-ver-com-ing grace, I am

fore me wide-ly swung de-struction's door; But the Shepherd of my soul,
weak-ness of my na-ture I de-plore, I am cling-ing to the hand,
ny the precious "Name" that I a-dore; I re-joice that I am saved,
press-ing on to-ward the shin-ing shore; There I'll read a welcome home,

Turned my face to-ward the fold, And I learned to love my Sav-ior
That has borne my guilt a-way, And I trust my dear Re-deem-er
From the pleasures that de-file, And I prize my sin-less Je-sus
In my el-der Brother's face, And for-ev-er love my Sav-ior

CHORUS.

more and more. More and more, ... yes, more and more,

More and more,   yes, more and more,

I de-sire to love my Sav-ior more and more;

yes, more and more;

58

MORE AND MORE. Concluded.

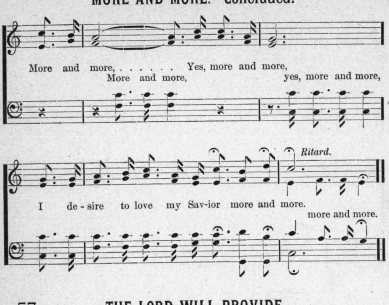

More and more, ... Yes, more and more,
More and more,   yes, more and more,

Ritard.

I de - sire to love my Sav-ior more and more.
                              more and more.

57.   THE LORD WILL PROVIDE.

MRS. M. A. W. COOK.   E. S. LORENZ.

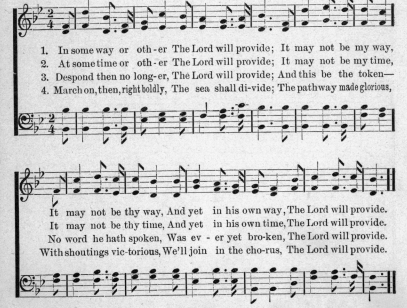

1. In some way or oth-er The Lord will provide; It may not be my way,
2. At some time or oth-er The Lord will provide; It may not be my time,
3. Despond then no long-er, The Lord will provide; And this be the token—
4. March on, then, right boldly, The sea shall di-vide; The pathway made glorious,

It may not be thy way, And yet in his own way, The Lord will provide.
It may not be thy time, And yet in his own time, The Lord will provide.
No word he hath spoken, Was ev - er yet bro-ken, The Lord will provide.
With shoutings vic-torious, We'll join in the cho-rus, The Lord will provide.

59

58. LIFT THE GOSPEL BANNER.

Arranged by C. A. S.

C. A. SHAW.

1. Lift the gos - pel ban - ner, Wave it far and wide, Thro' the crowded
2. Lift the gos - pel standard, Spread the gos - pel light, Let the blessed
3. Let us rise to ac - tion, Work with one design, Work with Christ and

cit - y, O - ver o - cean's tide; Sound the proc - la - ma - tion,
ra - diance, Flame o'er heath-en night. Love is God's own sun - shine,
tri - umph, In the work di - vine. Vic-t'ry's palms a - wait us,

Peace to all mankind! Je - sus and sal - va - tion, All the world may find.
Such as an-gels prove, Conquer men by kind-ness, God him-self is love.
Let us then work on, Till we hear the wel-come, Faith-ful ones, well done.

CHORUS.

Lift . . . . . . the gos - pel ban - - ner! Let the
Lift the gos - pel banner! Lift the gos - pel banner!

tid-ings of sal - va - tion roll! Lift . . . . . . the gos - pel
Lift the gos - pel banner!

LIFT THE GOSPEL BANNER. Concluded.

ban - - ner! Till its glo - ry spreads from pole to pole.
Lift the gos - pel ban - ner!

59. WE SING OF A LAND.

FANNY J. CROSBY.   ADAM GEIBEL.

1. We sing of a land that is love - ly and bright, We sing of a
2. We sing of a land where they hun - ger no more, Where sor - row and
3. We sing of a land that is hap - py and blest, A land where the

home in its man-sions of light; That Je - sus our Sav - ior has
weep-ing and tri - als are o'er; A land that from sin and temp-
wea - ry from la - bor shall rest; O Sav-ior, dear Sav - ior, our

gone to pre - pare, For those who are faith - ful to
ta - tion is free, And they who are faith - ful u -
guide wilt thou be, That we may be gath - ered for -

D.S.—*Where they who are faith - ful shall*

FINE.   CHORUS.   D.S.

dwell with him there.)
nit - ed shall be. } Beau - ti - ful land   o - ver the tide,
ev - er with thee.)

ev - er a - bide.

61

60. SEEING JESUS ONLY.

E. E. HEWITT.   ARTHUR W. NELSON.

Not too fast.

1. See - ing Je - sus on - ly, as my great High Priest, By his blest a -
2. See - ing Je - sus on - ly, as my Pat - tern true; Let his life of
3. See - ing Je - sus on - ly, as my Prince of Peace, Calming stormy

tonement, from my sin re-leased; Look-ing un - to Cal-v'ry, call-ing
beau - ty show me what to do; Al- ways helping oth-ers, meek, for-
wa - ters, bid-ding tu- mult cease; Pray- ing for his kingdom, liv-ing

on his name, Je - sus, pre-cious Sav- ior, will the lost re-claim.
giv - ing, kind, May I, by his Spir - it, have the Mas - ter's mind.
as I pray I shall see him com- ing down the shin - ing way.

D.S.—*Je - sus is my Sav- ior, ev - er more the same.*

f CHORUS.

Je - sus on - ly! at his cross I fall; Je - sus only! "crown him

Lord of all!" Looking un- to Cal- v'ry, glo - ry to his name,

THE BOOK OF TRUTH.

W. F. MCCAULEY.   SAM'L MITCHELL.

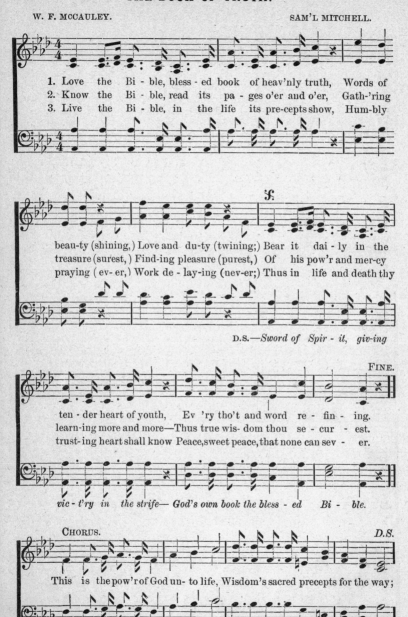

1. Love the Bi - ble, bless - ed book of heav'nly truth, Words of
2. Know the Bi - ble, read its pa - ges o'er and o'er, Gath-'ring
3. Live the Bi - ble, in the life its pre-cepts show, Hum-bly

beau-ty (shining,) Love and du-ty (twining;) Bear it dai - ly in the
treasure (surest,) Find-ing pleasure (purest,) Of his pow'r and mer-cy
praying (ev- er,) Work de - lay-ing (nev-er;) Thus in life and death thy

D.S.—*Sword of Spir - it, giv-ing*

FINE.

ten - der heart of youth, Ev 'ry tho't and word re - fin - ing.
learn-ing more and more—Thus true wis- dom thou se - cur - est.
trust-ing heart shall know Peace, sweet peace, that none can sev - er.

vic - t'ry in the strife— God's own book the bless - ed Bi - ble.

CHORUS.   D.S.

This is the pow'r of God un- to life, Wisdom's sacred precepts for the way;

62. THE FOLD OF THE BLEST.

WM. H. GARDNER.

J. HOWARD ENTWISLE.

Slow and with great expression.

1. There's a voice in the wil - der - ness cry - ing for help, 'Tis some
2. There's a dim light still shin - ing far out on the moor, But, O
3. Tho' the night set - tles round ye, your work is not o'er, For some

wea - ry one long-ing and pray-ing for rest; Oh, then go ye and
see how it flick-ers for hope is near gone; Come, then kindly love's
sheep may be dy-ing a - lone in the cold; There is time yet to

search for the wan-der-ing sheep, And bring it a - gain to the
bea - con and point out the way, To the "Fold of the Blest," where each
save them, press on thro' the dark, And bring them to rest in the

CHORUS. *Faster.*

"Fold of the Blest."
heart throb-beth warm.
midst of the fold.

O the Fold of the Blest, Shelter-ing

fold of the blest, Where the weak are se-cure, And the wea - ry find rest;

O the fold of the blest, Glo - ri - ous fold of the blest,

rit.

With the Shepherd true and ten - der, In the fold of the blest.

63.   O JESUS, LET US HELP.

REV. H. J. ZELLEY.   E. S. LORENZ.

1. The ran-som price is ful - ly paid, Thou hast for sin atonement made,
2. We want to bear thy precious word, To those who ne'er be-fore have heard,
3. As thou dost seek the ones a-stray, To guide them back in - to the way;

S.   FINE.

But if thou need-est hu - man aid, O Je-sus, let us help.
Till ev - 'ry hu - man heart is stirr'd; O Je-sus, let us help.
We would as-sist thee if we may—O Je-sus, let us help.

D.S.—*Our lov - ing hearts will al - ways pray, O Je - sus, let us help.*

CHORUS.   D.S.

Je - sus, let us help! . . . Je - sus, let us help! . .
O let us help!   O let us help!

R. of G. 5 R. N.

64. WATCHING FOR THE MORNING.

THOMAS WATSON.   CHAS. H. GABRIEL.

1. The dark-ness fades away, and the morn draws nigh, When the shadows of the
2. My eyes may close in sleep ere the break of day, But the Lord will wake me
3. The morn will soon be here with its joy and light And the glo-ry of the

night will fall no more; And an end-less day will cheer each wist-ful eye,
when he comes a-gain; When he comes to call me home to him for aye,
day will shine a-far; Then our watching eyes will gladden at the sight

CHORUS.

And the wea-ry watch of life is o'er.
In his glo-ry ev-er-more to reign.   }   I am watching for the
When we rise and hail the Morn-ing Star.

morn-ing When the end-less morn will break When the brightness of his

glo-ry we shall see, ... When we'll see the Lord returning, All his
we shall see,

WATCHING FOR THE MORNING. Concluded.

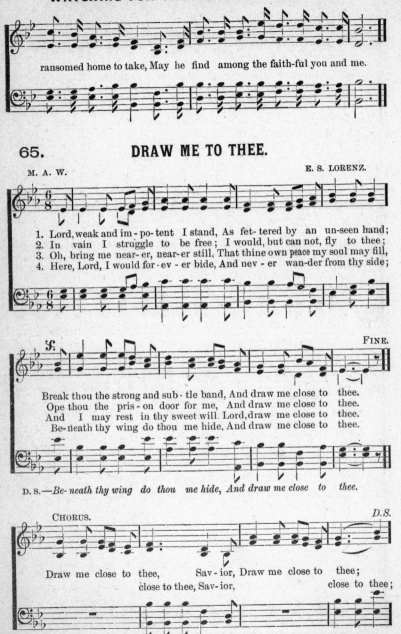

ransomed home to take, May he find among the faith-ful you and me.

65. DRAW ME TO THEE.

M. A. W.

E. S. LORENZ.

1. Lord, weak and im-po-tent I stand, As fet-tered by an un-seen hand;
2. In vain I struggle to be free; I would, but can not, fly to thee;
3. Oh, bring me near-er, near-er still, That thine own peace my soul may fill,
4. Here, Lord, I would for-ev-er bide, And nev-er wan-der from thy side;

FINE.

Break thou the strong and sub-tle band, And draw me close to thee.
Ope thou the pris-on door for me, And draw me close to thee.
And I may rest in thy sweet will. Lord, draw me close to thee.
Be-neath thy wing do thou me hide, And draw me close to thee.

D. S.—*Be-neath thy wing do thou me hide, And draw me close to thee.*

CHORUS.

D. S.

Draw me close to thee, Sav-ior, Draw me close to thee;
close to thee, Sav-ior, close to thee;

66.
THE ONLY WAY HOME.

MRS. FRANK A. BRECK.
ARTHUR W. NELSON.

Moderato.

1. O Christ is the "Way and the Truth and the Life" With him none in
2. To bring him the bur-dens he promised to bear— To trust in his
3. In time of temp-ta-tion the Sav-ior is nigh, And giv-eth his
4. O ye who are lost on the o-cean of sin, Tossed high on the
5. My song of re-joic-ing for-ev-er shall be, Be-neath heaven's

darkness shall roam; He com-forts all sor-row, he heal-eth all strife,
mer-cy a-lone— To take all the blessings he of-fers to share—
strength to o'er-come; In doubt or in dan-ger he ev-er stands by
bil-low-ing foam; The life-boat is com-ing, let Christ take you in,
glo-ri-ous dome, That Je-sus brought joy and sal-va-tion to me,

CHORUS.

And he is the on-ly way home.
O that is the on-ly way home.
To show us the on-ly way home.
And show you the on-ly way home.
And showed me the on-ly way home.

The on-ly way home, the

on-ly way home, Take Je-sus the on-ly way home! There's

on - ly one way—O take it to-day—Take Jesus the on-ly way home.

67.

GOD OVER ALL.

E. E. HEWITT.

E. S. LORENZ.

1. The sea-sons come, the sea-sons go, The ros - es bloom and fall ; The
2. Sweet mercies, like the springing flow'rs, Our grateful hearts recall, His
3. Life onward moves with changing scenes, And hopes, like blossoms fall ; But
4. We'll serve the Lord thro' rain and shine, Un-til we hear his call ; Then

FINE.

grass - es hide be - neath the snow, But God is o - ver all.
grace de-cends in fruit- ful show'rs, And God is o - ver all.
faith this pre - cious com- fort gleans, That God is o - ver all.
prais- ing him for love di - vine, Sing, God is o - ver all.

D.S.—deem- ing love Bears rule a - bove, And God is o - ver all.

REFRAIN.

D.S.

O-ver all, blessed for - ev - er, O-ver all, blessed for - ev - er ; Re-
O-ver all, O-ver all,

69

68. REAPING AS YOU GO.

FANNY J. CROSBY.

E. S. LORENZ.

1. Press on - ward, Christian work - ers, To la - bor with your might,
2. Press on - ward, Christian work - ers, The Mas-ter gives com - mand;
3. Press on to work for Je - sus, As you have ne'er be - fore,

The morn-ing sun is shin - ing, The har-vest fields are white.
Waste not a sin - gle mo - ment, But toil with heart and hand.
There's la - bor all a - round you, 'Tis e - ven at your door.

If you are friends of Je - sus, Then haste your love to show,
Be - hold the sheaves are wav - ing, And fruits of prom - ise grow,
Oh, lead the faint and wea - ry, Where life's pure wa - ters flow,

Press on-ward, still re - joic - ing, And reap-ing as you go.
Press on-ward, then, re - joic - ing, And reap-ing as you go.
Press on-ward, still re - joic - ing, And reap-ing as you go.

CHORUS.

Reap - ing as you go, . . . Reap - ing as you go!
Reap - ing as you go, Reap - ing as you go!

Oh, what rapt-ure you shall know, As reap-ing on you go.

69. ## IN THE LIGHT OF ETERNITY.

W. S. M.

W. S. MARTIN.

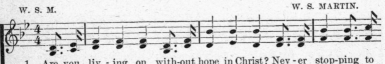

1. Are you liv-ing on with-out hope in Christ? Nev-er stop-ping to
2. What-so-e'er you do, wher-so-e'er you go, In the dark-ness or
3. It is sometimes good, it is sometimes ill, That you meet on this

think or pray? Give your soul some thought and be-gin to live
in the day, Heed the call of God, and do all your work
world's high-way; It will all come right, if you live for Christ

D.S.—*Heed the call of God and do all you can,*

FINE. CHORUS.

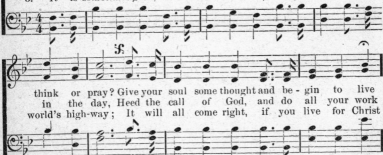

In the light of e-ter-ni-ty. You should live
you should live,

In the light of e-ter-ni-ty.

D.S.

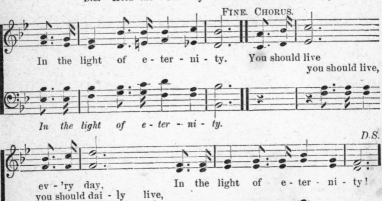

ev-'ry day, In the light of e-ter-ni-ty!
you should dai-ly live,

70. LISTEN TO THE SAVIOR'S VOICE!

WILLIAM H. GARDNER.

ADAM GEIBEL.

1. There's rest for you at Je - sus' feet, Lis ten to the Sav- ior's voice!
2. Oh, wand'rer on the mountain-side, Lis-ten to the Sav- ior's voice!
3. "Come, wea-ry ones, to me and rest!" Lis-ten to the Sav- ior's voice!

Oh, hear to - day the prom- ise sweet, Lis-ten to the Sav- ior's voice!
Let Je - sus be your heav'nly guide! Lis-ten to the Sav- ior's voice!
Come, sad hearts, to his bos - om blest, Lis-ten to the Sav- ior's voice!

Lay down your heav-y grief and care, The Lord will all your bur-dens bear,
'Tis but a step to joy and light, Come take it then, O friend, to-night!
Life's jour-ney now is near - ly o'er, See yon-der is the heav'nly shore,

For you, he died on Cal-v'ry there, Lis-ten to the Sav- ior's voice!
The " Path of Peace " dawns on your sight, Lis-ten to the Sav- ior's voice!
There joy a - waits you ev - er more, Lis-ten to the Sav- ior's voice!

CHORUS.

Lis - ten to his gen-tle voice! Hear him
Lis - ten to his voice, Lis-ten to his voice, Hear him calling

LISTEN TO THE SAVIOR'S VOICE! Concluded.

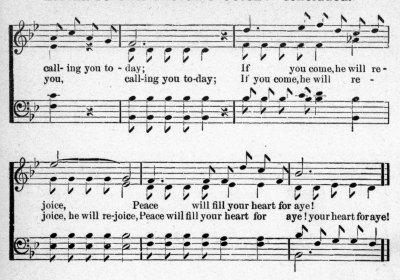

call- ing you to - day;   If   you come, he will re-
you,   call-ing you to-day;   If you come, he will   re -

joice,   Peace   will fill your heart for aye!
joice, he will re-joice, Peace will fill your heart for   aye! your heart for aye!

7l.   I CAN NOT DO WITHOUT THEE.

FRANCES R. HAVERGAL.   E. S. LORENZ.

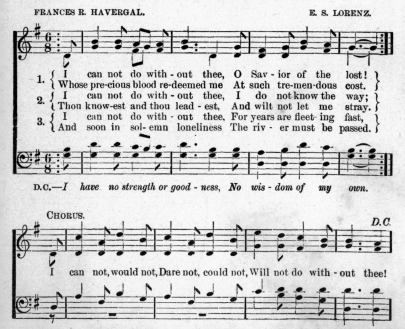

1. { I   can not do with - out thee, O Sav - ior of the   lost! }
   { Whose pre-cious blood re-deemed me At such tre-men-dous cost. }
2. { I   can not do with - out thee, I   do not know the   way; }
   { Thou know-est and thou lead - est, And wilt not let me   stray. }
3. { I   can not do with - out thee, For years are fleet-ing fast, }
   { And soon in sol-emn loneliness The riv - er must be passed. }

D.C.—*I have no strength or good - ness, No wis - dom of my   own.*

CHORUS.   *D.C.*

I   can not, would not, Dare not, could not, Will not do with - out thee!

72. PREPARE YE THE WAY OF THE LORD.

FANNY J. CROSBY.

W. H. DOANE.

1. The Lord is com-ing, our Re-deem-er, King, Whose voice the world shall hear; The Lord is com-ing, let the sound go forth,
2. The Lord is com-ing, our Re-deem-er, King, To set his peo-ple free; In him the prom-ise of the a-ges past,
3. The Lord is com-ing, our Re-deem-er, King, O'er heav'n and earth to reign; His arm shall tri-umph o'er op-pres-sion's pow'r,

REFRAIN.

Be-hold! the time is near.) Pre-pare ye the way of the Lord,
A light that all may see. } of the Lord,
And break the captives chain.)

Pre-pare ye the way of the Lord; Make straight in the desert, make
of the Lord,

straight in the des-ert, A high-way for our God, our Lord.
our God,

73. LOVE FOUND ME!

E. R. LATTA.   CHAS. K. LANGLEY.

1. In the paths of sin a-stray, Love found me! love found me!
2. Car-ing naught that Je-sus died, Love found me! love found me!
3. Oh, how bless-ed was my state, Love found me! love found me!

DUET.

Tho' I'd wandered far a-way, Love found me! In my want and
On the mountain, cru-ci-fied, Love found me! Thoughtless of the
When I yield-ed, tho' so late! Love found me! From the nar-row

wretched-ness, Love found me! love found me! And I felt no
pain he bore, Love found me! love found me! That he might the
path a-way. Love found me! love found me! Let me go no

CHORUS.

more dis-tress! Love found me!
lost re-store, Love found me! } Love di-vine my soul o'ercame,
more a-stray! Love found me!

And that love is still the same! Blessed be Je-hovah's name! Love found me!

74. SEND THE LIGHT.

W. M. B.

REV. W. M. BELL, D. D.

1. See now the waves that bathe the shores, Re-flect-ing light the sun out - pours; So in all lands be- neath the sun, The reign of day is now be - gun.

2. The lands long dark by Sa-tan's night Sad-ly a - wait the com- ing light; There millions sink in dead- ly dread, No pil- low sure for dy - ing head.

3. Too long the light have we with - held, Whose rays their night would have dis - pelled; Speed on the day, the glo-rious day, Thro' Christ, the Light, the Truth, the Way.

CHORUS.

Send the light, ... Oh, send it on! . . . . Till all lands . . . . . . take up the song; . . . . . . See the suf - - - f'ring where they

Oh, send the light, Oh, send it on! lands take up the song, Yes, till all lands take up the song; See the suff'ring where they fall. Yes, all the

SEND THE LIGHT. Concluded.

fall, ... Hear, oh, hear . . . their pleading call.
suff'ring where they fall, their pleading,

75. OPEN YOUR HEART.

F. L. SNYDER. GEO. E. MYERS.

1. O-pen your heart ev'ry morning, Turn not the Saviour a-way;
2. O-pen your heart ev'ry morning Full to the Spirit's con-trol;
3. O-pen your heart ev'ry morning, How can past blessings suf-fice?

Let him prepare you for ser-vice, Which you may ren-der that day.
Add to your faith and your graces, Fill with new pow-er your soul.
Seek a fresh glimpse of the Mas-ter, Yours without mon-ey or price.

CHORUS.

O- - pen, o- - pen, O-pen your heart to each ray;
O- pen your heart, o- pen your heart,

Bask in the sunlight of Je - sus, And he will bless you to - day.

77

76. SPREAD THE NEWS.

F. S. SHEPARD.

E. S. LORENZ.

1. Je - sus came the lost to find, Spread the news! spread the news!
2. Christ a - lone for sin a - tones, Spread the news! spread the news!
3. "Who - so - ev - er will may come," Spread the news! spread the news!
4. "Christ hath pow'r on earth to save." Spread the news! spread the news!

Gave him - self for all man - kind, Spread the bless - ed gos - pel news!
And the pow'r of sin dethrones, Spread the bless - ed gos - pel news!
Christ will wel - come each one home, Spread the bless - ed gos - pel news!
'Twas for this his life he gave, Spread the bless - ed gos - pel news!

Yes, he hung up - on the tree, That from sin we might be free;
He hath paid the price for all Who are ru - ined by the fall;
What a won - drous love and rare, That the wand'rers from God's care
Send the truth the world a - round, Where-so - ev - er sin is found,

Died to ran - som you and me, Spread the bless - ed gos - pel news!
Saves, when on his name they call, Spread the bless - ed gos - pel news!
May his rich - est bless - ings share, Spread the bless - ed gos - pel news!
That God's grace may there a - bound, Spread the bless - ed gos - pel news!

CHORUS.

Spread the news, that the world may hear! Spread the news broken hearts to cheer!

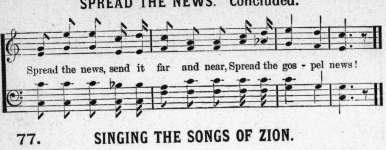

Spread the news, send it far and near, Spread the gos - pel news!

77. SINGING THE SONGS OF ZION.

JENNIE WILSON.

ADAM GEIBEL.

1. Trusting in Je - sus thro' life I go, Sing-ing the songs of Zi - on,
2. Glad - ly I rest in his prom-ise sure, Sing-ing the songs of Zi - on,
3. Res cued by mer-cy, time's vale I roam, Sing-ing the songs of Zi - on,
4. Faith views a cit - y on heaven's shore, Beau - ti - ful, ho - ly Zi - on,

Tread-ing my pil-grim path here be - low, Sing-ing the songs of Zi - on.
Know-ing he keep-eth me e'er se - cure, Sing-ing the songs of Zi - on.
Prais-ing my Sav - ior I'll jour-ney home, Sing-ing the songs of Zi - on.
There I shall dwell thro' the ev - er - more, Sing-ing the songs of Zi - on.

CHORUS.

Brightly the light in my soul doth shine, Happy in knowing Christ's love is mine;

Close - ly I cling to his hand di - vine, Sing-ing the songs of Zi - on.

78. ANYWHERE WITH JESUS.

MAGGIE E. GREGORY.

CHAS. H. GABRIEL.

1. An-y-where with Je-sus I will glad-ly go; If he will but
2. An-y-where with Je-sus, ev-en tho' I know Thro' the vale of
3. An-y-where with Je-sus, when he bids me lay All up-on the

lead me, fear I can-not know; Walking in his foot-steps noth-ing
suff-'ring I am called to go: Sor-row, borne for him will prove a
al-tar, and his call o-bey; Ful-ly con-se-cra-ted, I have

can mo-lest, Lean-ing on his bo-som I shall find sweet rest.
bless-ing sweet: Wel-come be the pain that keeps me at his feet.
peace with-in, And the blood of Je-sus cleans-eth me from sin.

Chorus.

I will go, I will go, yes, an-y-where with Je-sus I will

go, ... I will go an-y-where; This my cry shall be Thro'
I will go,

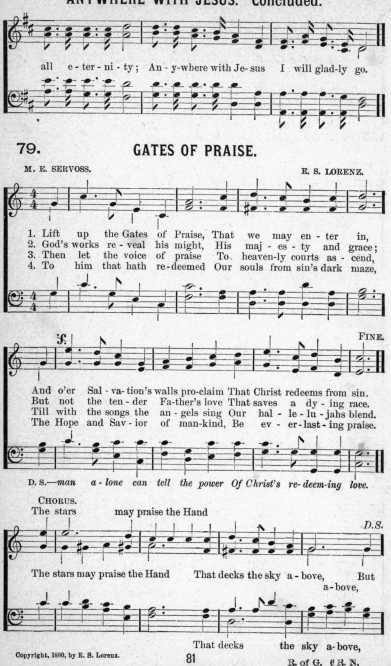

all e-ter-ni-ty; An-y-where with Je-sus I will glad-ly go.

79. GATES OF PRAISE.

M. E. SERVOSS.   E. S. LORENZ.

1. Lift up the Gates of Praise, That we may en - ter in,
2. God's works re - veal his might, His maj - es - ty and grace;
3. Then let the voice of praise To heaven-ly courts as - cend,
4. To him that hath re-deemed Our souls from sin's dark maze,

FINE.

And o'er Sal - va-tion's walls pro-claim That Christ redeems from sin.
But not the ten - der Fa-ther's love That saves a dy - ing race.
Till with the songs the an - gels sing Our hal - le - lu - jahs blend.
The Hope and Sav - ior of man-kind, Be ev - er-last - ing praise.

D. S.—man a - lone can tell the power Of Christ's re-deem-ing love.

CHORUS.
The stars may praise the Hand

D.S.

The stars may praise the Hand That decks the sky a - bove, But
a - bove,

That decks the sky a - bove,

R. of G. CR. N.

80. I'LL BE TRUE TO MY SAVIOR.

REV. H. J. ZELLEY.   E. S. LORENZ.

1. I am trusting Christ my Sav-ior and I know he's trust-ing me,
2. Ev-'ry task the Sav-iour gives me on-ly brings me great-er joy,
3. O, I love to live for Je-sus, love his will a-lone to do,

For I try each pass-ing moment, more and more like him to be;
And I love, for Christ my Sav-ior, all my pow-ers to em-ploy;
And, wher-e'er my path-way lead-eth, still to him I will be true;

When he points to me a du-ty, quick-ly then do I o-bey,
Noth-ing gives me great-er pleas-ure than to serve him as I may,
What he says, I'll glad-ly do it, when he points, I'll quick-ly go,

For I love to do his bid-ding and to serve him day by day.
Do some lit-tle thing to please him as I pass a-long the way.
For I find in serv-ing Je-sus great-er bliss than earth can know.

CHORUS.

I'll be true!   I'll be true!   Ev-'ry
     to my Sav-ior,   to my Sav-ior,

I'LL BE TRUE TO MY SAVIOR. Concluded.

day and ev-'ry hour I'll be true; From no dan-ger will I
I'll be true;

flee, faithful to my Lord I'll be, In the sunshine or the darkness I'll be true.

81. GERAR.

S. STENNETT.
Moderato.

LOWELL MASON.

1. How charming is the place Where my Re - deem - er God
2. Here, on the mer - cy - seat, With ra - diant glo - ry crowned,
3. To him their pray'rs and cries, Each con - trite soul pre - sents;
4. Give me, O Lord, a place With - in thy blest a - bode;

Un - veils the glo - ries of his face, Un - veils the
Our joy - ful eyes be - hold him sit, Our joy - ful
And while he hears their hum - ble sighs, And while he
A - mong the chil - dren of thy grace, A - mong the

glo - ries of his face, And sheds his love a - broad!
eyes be - hold him sit, And smile on all a - round.
bears their hum - ble sighs, He grants them all their wants.
chil - dren of thy grace, The serv - ants of my God.

82. LEAD ME ALL THE WAY.

W. A. O.   W. A. OGDEN.

1. Sav-ior, lead me all the way, Lest from the path of peace I stray;
2. Thou my ref-uge art from sin, Let me thy pre-cious fa-vor win;
3. When the storms of life are past, When to the grave I come, at last;

1. Near .... thy side ....
2. Sav - - ior blest ....
3. Lord, ... I pray ...

Close to thee I would a-bide, Near to thy wounded, wounded side.
In thine arms of love I'd rest, Sav-ior, oh lov-ing Sav-ior blest.
Be thou still my hope and stay, Sav-ior, I hum-bly, hum-bly pray.

REFRAIN.

Lead me, O Sav-ior, Day by day, day by day;

Lead me, O Sav-ior, All .... the way ....
All the way, yes, all the way.

CHEER UP.

E. D. MUND.

E. S. LORENZ.

1. The birds are all sing-ing, The flow'r-bells are ring-ing, Cheer
2. With all things re - joic - ing, Their hap - pi - ness voic-ing, Cheer
3. A - way with your sad - ness, Drink deep of life's glad-ness, Cheer

up, cheer up, cheer up! Oh, cease your re - pin - ing, The glad sun is
up, cheer up, cheer up! The Spring breezes blow-ing, New life are be -
up, cheer up, cheer up! Your fears all surmounting, Your mer-cies re -

shin - ing, Cheer up! cheer up! cheer up! The for - ests sing their tri -
stow-ing, Cheer up! cheer up! cheer up! Re - joice, be glad, is the
count-ing, Cheer up! cheer up! cheer up! Our God is liv - ing, a

umph-ant song, The o - cean rais-es its voice so strong; O'er all the
Lord's command; When earth obeys, lifts a cho - rus grand, Should we in
help in need, Our God is lov-ing, a friend in-deed; Our great-est

earth joins a count-less throng, Cheer up! cheer up! cheer up! cheer up!
heav - i - ness, song-less stand! Cheer up! cheer up! cheer up! cheer up!
hope will his grace ex - ceed, Cheer up! cheer up! cheer up! cheer up!

84. THE POWER OF JEHOVAH'S ARM.

G. M. BILIS.

M. L. McPHAIL.

1. When the del- uge had bur- ied the mountains crest, And the wreckage of
2. When the prophets of Baal of their fren - zy tire, And the Al-mighty
3. When the fur- nace was white with the fier - y glow, And the servants of
4. When the ser- vants of Saul saw their lead - er fall, Stricken down to the
5. Thus the rec- ords di- vine put our fears to shame, As we fol-low our

sin strewed its heav - ing breast, There was mirrored the har - vest of
God answers pray'r by fire; When the flames lick the earth and the
God to their fate did go; Lo, the An - gel of God to the
earth by the heav'n-ly call; Saw the foe of the saints by the
God in - to flood and flame; They who have for their Cap - tain the

slight- ed grace And the hand of the Lord on a guilt - y race:
trench-es dry, "Serve the God of E - li - jah" the peo - ple cry:
res - cue came While the He- brews re-joiced in the harm - less flame:
Priest-hood spurned, And a hat - er of Christ to a Christ-ian turned:
Kings of Kings, Un - to vic - to - ry rise, as on ea- gle's wings.

CHORUS.

They have witnessed the pow'r of Je- ho- vah's arm As it cir- cles the

might - y sea and shore; And re-mind us that God can his

foes dis-arm, And de-liv - er his chil - dren for - ev - er-more.

85. I HAVE REDEEMED THEE!

E. R. LATTA.   ADAM GEIBEL.

1. Sin-ner, far a-way from God, I have redeemed thee! By the shedding
2. From the bondage of thy sin, I have redeemed thee! That thou migh'st be
3. From the fate that was thy due, I have redeemed thee! That thou migh'st my

of my blood, I have redeemed thee! Wilt thou not in me believe, O'er thy
pure with-in, I have redeemed thee! Wilt thou now repent, indeed, Feeling
steps pur-sue, I have redeemed thee! Wilt thou take my cross to-day? Wilt thou

sins and fol-lies grieve, And e - ter-nal life receive? I have redeemed thee!
all thy loss and need, While for thee I in-ter-cede? I have redeemed thee!
bear it all the way? Thou shalt reign in heav'n for aye! I have redeemed thee!

86. REDEMPTION DRAWETH NIGH.

PRISCILLA J. OWENS.

E. S. LORENZ.

1. A - bove the storms of earth, I hear the trumpets sound The news of
2. Then righteousness and truth, Shall grow in ev - 'ry land, And hap-py,
3. Then flow-ers pure and bright A - round this path shall spring, And stars bow

joy and mirth, To all the realms a-round. The voice of ju - bi-lee Is
faith-ful youth, Rise up on ev - 'ry hand. Then peaceful, glad employ, In
down to light The coming of the King. Then let us watch and pray, And

heard on hill and plain; From sin to set us free, The Sav-ior comes to reign.
ev-'ry home shall be; No wast-er shall destroy, God makes his peo - ple free.
wait the joyful sound; The King is on his way, Proclaim the news a-round.

CHORUS.

For the breath of God shall blow, And the liv-ing wa-ters flow,
blow, shall blow, waters flow,

And the tear be wiped from ev - 'ry eye: Our re-demption draweth nigh.

ZION IN TRIUMPH.

T. HASTINGS.

CHAS. H. GABRIEL.

1. Hail to the bright-ness of Zi-on's glad morn-ing! Joy to the lands
2. Lo, in the des - ert rich flowers are springing; Streams ev-er co-
3. See, from all lands, from the isles of the o - cean, Praise to Je - ho -

that in darkness have lain! Hushed be the ac - cents of sor-row and
pious are glid-ing a - long; Loud from the mount-ain-tops ech-oes are
vah as-cend-ing on high; Fal-len the en - gines of war and com-

%.

FINE.

mourn - ing, Zi - on in tri - umph be - gins her glad reign.
ring - ing Wastes rise in ver - dure, and min - gle in song.
mo - tion, Shouts of sal - va - tion are rend-ing the sky.

D.S.—Zi - on in tri - umph be - gins her glad reign.

CHORUS.

Hail to the brightness, hail! Zi-on shall yet prevail, Let ev-'ry mor-tal tongue

D.S.

catch up the strain, Hushed be the ac - cents of sor-row and mourning,

88. WHY NOT DECIDE TO-DAY?

ROBERT H. WALTON.

CHAS. H. GABRIEL.

1. Come to the Sav-ior, he's pleading for thee! Why not de-cide to-
2. Come, there is mer-cy for all who be-lieve, Why not de-cide to-
3. Why not de-cide to for-sake ev-'ry sin— Why not de-cide to-

day? (to-day?) Wait-ing and long-ing your soul to set free,
day? (to-day?) Lin-ger no long-er, the Sav-ior to grieve,
day? (to-day?) Je-sus will help you the vic-t'ry to win,

Why not de-cide to-day? (to-day?) He is a friend that is
Why not de-cide to-day? (to-day?) Moments are pass-ing—the
Why not de-cide to-day? (to-day?) An-gels are wait-ing to

faith-ful and true, What he has promised he sure-ly will do;
days go-ing by, Shad-ows are gath-er-ing o-ver the sky!
tell the glad news; Do not, O do not the Sav-ior re-fuse;

FINE.

Trust him, O sinner, and come while you may, Why not decide to-day? (to-day?)
Come while the Savior is pass-ing this way! Why not decide to-day? (to-day?)
Come and accept him—there's nothing to pay, Why not decide to-day? (to-day?)

D.S.—*He is a friend that is faithful and true— Why not decide to-day? (to-day?)*

WHY NOT DECIDE TO-DAY? Concluded.

D.S.

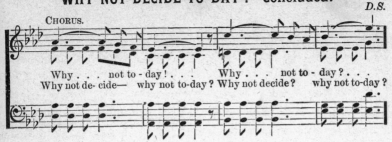

CHORUS.

Why . . . not to - day ! . . .   Why . . . not to - day ? . . .
Why not de- cide—   why not to-day ? Why not decide ?   why not to-day ?

89.   CLINGING TO THE SAVIOR.

CHAS. H. GABRIEL.   E. S. LORENZ.

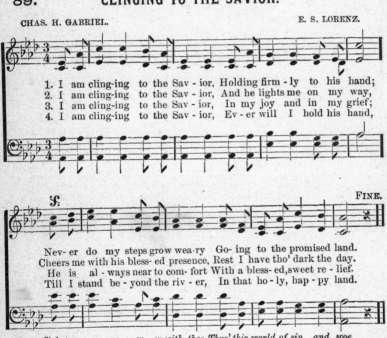

1. I am cling-ing   to the Sav - ior, Holding firm - ly   to   his hand;
2. I am cling-ing   to the Sav - ior, And he lights me on   my way,
3. I am cling-ing   to the Sav - ior, In my joy and in   my grief;
4. I am cling-ing   to the Sav - ior, Ev - er will I hold his hand,

Nev- er do my steps grow wea-ry Go- ing to the promised land.
Cheers me with his bless- ed presence, Rest I have tho' dark the day.
He is al - ways near to com- fort With a bless- ed,sweet re - lief.
Till I stand be - yond the riv - er, In that ho - ly, hap - py land.

D.S.—*Take me ev - er,   ev - er with thee, Thro' this world of sin and woe.*

CHORUS.   D.S.

Cling-ing, Sav - ior, cling-ing close - ly, Nev- er will I let thee go,

90. WORK FOR JESUS.

E. E. HEWITT.　　　　　　　　　　　　　　　　　　E. S. LORENZ.

1. Work, O, work for Je-sus, thro' all the gold-en hours, Bringing to his
2. Work, O, work for Je-sus, O let the word have wings, Wonderful the
3. Work, O, work for Je-sus, for "ye are not your own," Purchased on Mount

ser-vice your highest, noblest pow'rs; Serving your Redeemer, who bought you
mes-sage, from Jesus, King of kings; Send abroad the ti-dings of mer-cy,
Calv'ry, and saved by grace alone; Give him all the glo-ry, and, speeding

"with a price," Lay up-on his al - tar, the will-ing sac- ri - fice.
truth and love, Winning precious jew- els to gem a crown a - bove.
in his ways, Run up-on his er - rands with happy songs of praise.

CHORUS.

Ev -'ry day, ev -'ry hour, make the world your debtor; Giv - ing Christ

ev -'ry pow'r, help - ing men grow bet - ter! Work for Je - sus

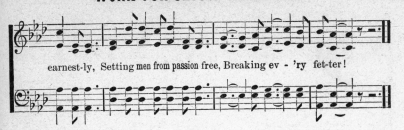

earnest-ly, Setting men from passion free, Breaking ev - 'ry fet-ter!

91.   WHO AT MY DOOR IS STANDING?

MRS. M. B. C. SLADE.   DR. A. B. EVERETT.

1. Who at my door is stand - ing,   Pa - tient - ly draw-ing near,
2. Lone - ly with-out he's stay - ing,   Lone - ly with-in am I;
3. All thro' the dark hours drear - y,   Knock-ing a - gain is he;
4. Door of my heart, I hast - en!   Thee will I o - pen wide;

En - trance with-in de - mand - ing?   Whose is the voice I hear?
While I am still de - lay - ing,   Will he not pass me by?
Je - sus, art thou not wea - ry   Wait - ing so long for me?
Tho' he re-buke and chas - ten,   He shall with me a - bide.

D.S.—*If thou wilt heed my call - ing,   I will a - bide with thee.*

REFRAIN.   D.S.

Sweet - ly the tones are fall - ing:— O - pen the door for me!

By per. R. M. McIntosh.

SABBATH HOURS.

FANNY J. CROSBY.

ADAM GEIBEL.

1. The Sab-bath hours, the Sab-bath hours, What hallowed peace they
2. The Sab-bath hours, the Sab-bath hours, God's mes-sen-gers of
3. The Sab-bath hours, the Sab-bath hours, Re-plete with tran-quil
4. The Sab-bath hours, the Sab-bath hours, A gra-cious God has

bring; How like the mes-sage-bird that bears Good news beneath its
love; He bids them bring to wait-ing hearts, Glad ti-dings from a -
rest, When pray'r and cheer-ful song a - rise, And kin-dred souls are
giv'n To lead us up the shin-ing way By steps of faith, to

wing. The harp of joy, in tune-ful strain, Its sil - ver
bove. The torch whose rays but dim - ly burn Re-kind - les
blest, And feel a pure and ho - ly joy Earth can - not
heav'n. Where souls re-deemed their voi - ces blend In that "new

tone a - wakes a-gain, Its sil - ver tone a - wakes a-gain.
in their bright re-turn, Re-kind - les in their bright re-turn.
give, nor Time de-stroy, Earth can-not give, nor Time de-stroy.
song" that ne'er shall end, In that "new song" that ne'er shall end.

EVERY DAY FOR JESUS.

MRS. ANNA W. CANTRALL.

E. L. ASHFORD.

1. Ev-'ry day to live for Je-sus, ev-ry day, (ev-'ry day,) Bringing
2. Ev-'ry day to live for Je-sus, ev-ry day, (ev-'ry day,) Counting
3. Ev-'ry day to live for Je-sus, ev-ry day, (ev-'ry day,) Help me

oth-ers to his feet, Bring-ing oth-ers to his feet, Teaching
ev-'ry loss a gain, Counting ev-'ry loss a gain, Giv-ing,
Lord that this may be, Help me Lord that this may be; Teach me

them to love and serve him ev-'ry day, (ev-'ry day,) Tell-ing
spend-ing with-out meas-ure, ev-'ry day, (ev-'ry day,) Do-ing
that in lov-ing ser-vice, ev-'ry day, (ev-'ry day,) I may

REFRAIN.

them the sto-ry sweet, Telling them the sto-ry sweet. ⎫ Ev'ry day,
all in his dear name, Doing all in his dear name. ⎬
spend my life for thee, I may spend my life for thee. ⎭ Ev-'ry day,

ev-'ry day, (ev'ry day,) Ev-'ry day to live for Je-sus, ev-'ry day.

GOD IS CALLING.

REV. S. W. COPE.   J. HOWARD ENTWISLE.

1. God is call-ing you to-day, Will you not the call o-bey? Come and
2. God is call-ing you to-day, From your sins to turn a-way; And from
3. God is call-ing you to-day, Whispers soft-ly, "Why de-lay:" Has-ten
4. God is call-ing you to-day, Call-ing, sinner, night and day; Come by

in his love con-fide, Mercy's door stands o-pen wide.
ev-'ry i-dol part, Lov-ing him with all your heart.
to the mer-cy seat, Here he waits your soul to greet.
faith his grace im-plore, Saved from guilt to sin no more.

CHORUS.
Yes, I come . . Yes, I come
Yes, I come, I come
Yes, I come

my God to thee, Saved by
now I come, Mer-cy is my on-ly plea;
my God to thee I come, Saved by
now I come,

grace . . . thro' love di-vine, . . .
Saved by grace love di-vine, I am now a child of thine.
grace, by grace thro' love di-vine, di-vine.
Saved by grace,

95. THE BOY'S BRIGADE.

JENNIE WILSON. ARTHUR W. NELSON.

1. We are sol-diers of right on the world's bat-tle field, O'er us waves the pure
2. We are sol-diers of right and we're marching a-long, Side by side on the
3. We are sol-diers of right and the foe we must meet, Face to face, but we
4. We are sol-diers of right and be-fore us there lies, To in-spire us, a

ban-ner of truth; To the cause we de-fend, till its en - e-mies yield,
King's roy-al way; As we strive in his ar - my to o - vercome wrong,
nev - er need fear; In the con - flict be-fore us we'll find no de-feat,
glo - ri-ous goal; Blessings rich from the King while on earth is the prize,

CHORUS.
ff Unison. With spirit.

We will give all the strength of our youth.
We his or - ders di-vine must o - bey.
As we list to the King's words of cheer.
And life's crown in the home of the soul.

We are sol - diers of right, let the

glad cho - rus ring, In the war-fare with wrong we will aid ; We have

entered the ser-vice of Je - sus the King In the ranks of the Boy's Brigade.

97

R. of G. 7 R. N.

96.

SING THEM O'ER.

L. B. M.

L. B. MITCHELL.

1. The songs of the great sal - va - tion, That our Sa - vior in
2. This life were a sad, sad jour - ney, Were it not for re -
3. Oh, praise ev - er more be ren - dered To the Source of all

love hath giv'n, Are the joy and de-light of pil - grims, Toil-ing
demptions song, That at-tunes thy poor heart to ser - vice, For to
hope and joy: In this life and thro' cease-less a - ges We shall

CHORUS.

on in the path - way to heav'n. }
Je - sus thy praise doth be - long. } Sing them o'er, ... Oh,
find in his praise sweet em - ploy. }

Sing them o'er,

sing them o'er, Songs of Je-sus' all redeeming love. Sing them
sing them o'er,

SING THEM O'ER. Concluded.

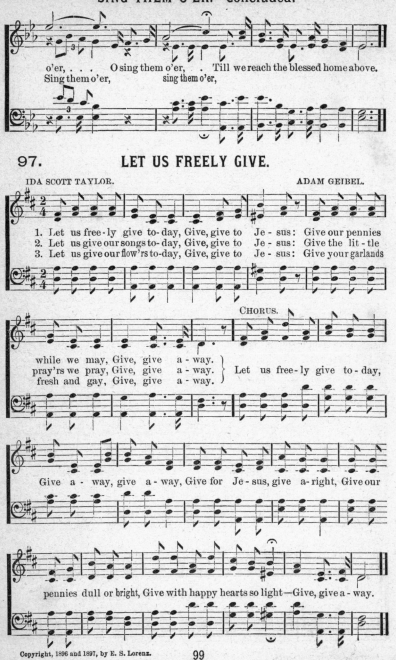

o'er, . . . O sing them o'er, . . Till we reach the blessed home above.

Sing them o'er,   sing them o'er,

97.   LET US FREELY GIVE.

IDA SCOTT TAYLOR.

ADAM GEIBEL.

1. Let us free-ly give to-day, Give, give to Je-sus: Give our pennies
2. Let us give our songs to-day, Give, give to Je-sus: Give the lit-tle
3. Let us give our flow'rs to-day, Give, give to Je-sus: Give your garlands

CHORUS.

while we may, Give, give a-way.   ⎫
pray'rs we pray, Give, give a-way.   ⎬ Let us free-ly give to-day,
fresh and gay, Give, give a-way.   ⎭

Give a-way, give a-way, Give for Je-sus, give a-right, Give our

pennies dull or bright, Give with happy hearts so light—Give, give a-way.

98. MANSIONS BRIGHT ABOVE.

J. CRANSTON.   W. A. OGDEN.

1. In my Fa-ther's house are man-sions fair, With glo-ry bright, and jew-els rare; I can sor-row bide, or bit-ter care—I've a man-sion bright a-bove.

2. Tho' the days may dark and gloom-y be, A-long the path God gives to me, Bright the glo-ry at the end I see— In the

3. Let us gath-er souls a-long the way; As sparkling jew-els in that day Shall they fail to shine in Christ's ar-ray? In the

CHORUS.

O time speed on, ... the glo-rious
O time speed on, the

way . . . Grows brighter ev - - ry pass-ing day; . . .
glo-rious way   Grows brighter ev - 'ry   pass-ing day;

To work for Je-sus while on earth I stay Shall be my great-est joy.

99. I WOULD WALK WITH JESUS.

H. F. JAMES.   E. S. LORENZ.

1. I would walk with Je - sus when morning hours are bright, When life's sun is
2. I would walk with Je - sus when sultry noontide beats, When life's burdens
3. I would walk with Je - sus when night approaches fast, And the sun's in

grand-ly ris - ing; For his pres-ence makes ev-'ry hour a deep de-light,
sore are press - ing; For with grace and love ev-'ry rising need he meets,
peace de - scend-ing; With my hand in his, soon the shadows will be past,

CHORUS.

A new joy each day sur-pris - ing;)
Crowns each hour of pain with bless- ing; } I would walk with Je - sus wher-
I shall share heav'n's bliss unend- ing;)

ev-er he may lead, Trusting him for all the way ; While with me he is a -

bid-ing, And my falt'ring foot-steps guiding, I can nev - er go a - stray.

100. THE BLOOD-BOUGHT HOPE.

G. M. BILLS. M. L. McPHAIL.

1. When I read the wondrous sto-ry of re-deem-ing grace, And the woes that overwhelmed the Lamb of God; I re-joice o'er all the blessings to a fal-len race, Springing from the path of pain the Sav-ior trod.

2. O how pre-cious was the ran-som that for all was paid, When the sin-less heart of Jesus ceased to beat; Since our wrath-de-serv-ing sinful-ness on him was laid, We are welcome to approach the mer-cy-seat.

3. O, I hear the an-gels sing-ing as they sang of old, And the mu-sic of their song shall never cease, Till the low-est child of er-ror may its truth be-hold, And sur-ren-der to the mighty Prince of Peace.

CHORUS.

Precious Bi - ble! from thy pa - ges,
Precious Bi-ble! from thy pa-ges, Precious Bi-ble! from thy pa-ges,

Shines the truth so grand and free,
Shines the truth so grand and free, Shines the truth so grand and free,

102

THE BLOOD-BOUGHT HOPE. Concluded.

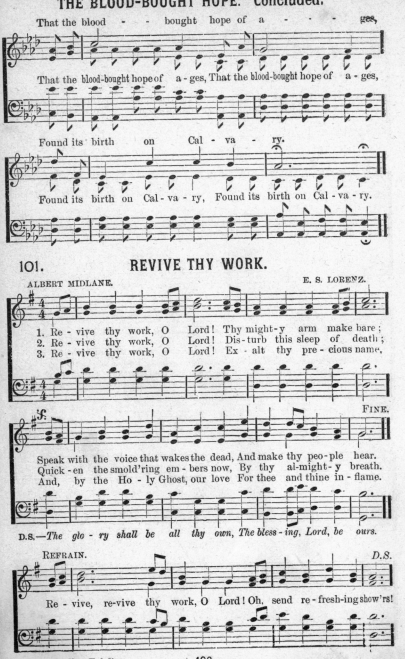

That the blood - - bought hope of a - - - ges,

That the blood-bought hope of a - ges, That the blood-bought hope of a - ges,

Found its birth on Cal - va - ry.

Found its birth on Cal - va - ry, Found its birth on Cal - va - ry.

101. REVIVE THY WORK.

ALBERT MIDLANE.   E. S. LORENZ.

1. Re - vive thy work, O Lord! Thy might-y arm make bare;
2. Re - vive thy work, O Lord! Dis-turb this sleep of death;
3. Re - vive thy work, O Lord! Ex-alt thy pre-cious name,

FINE.

Speak with the voice that wakes the dead, And make thy peo-ple hear.
Quick-en the smold'ring em-bers now, By thy al-might-y breath.
And, by the Ho-ly Ghost, our love For thee and thine in-flame.

D.S.—*The glo - ry shall be all thy own, The bless - ing, Lord, be ours.*

REFRAIN.   D.S.

Re - vive, re-vive thy work, O Lord! Oh, send re-fresh-ing show'rs!

LAMBS OF THE FOLD.

BIRDIE BELL.

E. S. LORENZ.

1. We are lambs of the fold, thro' the green fields we go, Where the flow - ers are
2. We are lambs of the fold, and we fol - low our Guide, As he leads us thro'
3. We are lambs of the fold and he keeps us from harm, He protects us from
4. We are lambs of his fold and we're near-er each day To the heav-en - ly

blooming, where still wa - ters flow; For 'tis Je - sus who leads us, yes,
fields where the clear wa - ters glide; And he calls us by name in a
dan - ger that oft would a-larm; O, our Shep-herd is lov - ing and
pastures where life's fountains play, Where the flow-ers in beau-ty un -

he is our Guide, And no dan - ger can harm us with him at our side.
voice low and sweet When we stray from the path he has mark'd for our feet.
ten - der to all Who will fol - low his lead-ing and an-swer his call.
fad - ing - ly blow, And his flock shall be fed where life's streams gen-tly flow.

CHORUS.

We are lambs of the fold, We are lambs of the fold, And the

Shep - herd in his bos - om all the weak ones will hold;

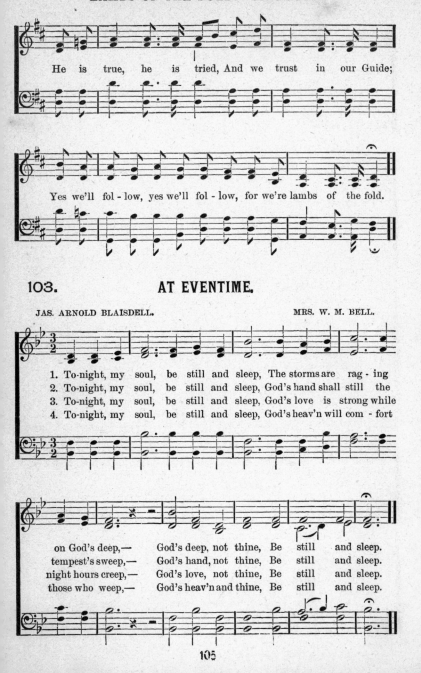

He is true, he is tried, And we trust in our Guide;

Yes we'll fol - low, yes we'll fol - low, for we're lambs of the fold.

103. ### AT EVENTIME.

JAS. ARNOLD BLAISDELL.   MRS. W. M. BELL.

1. To-night, my soul, be still and sleep, The storms are rag - ing
2. To-night, my soul, be still and sleep, God's hand shall still the
3. To-night, my soul, be still and sleep, God's love is strong while
4. To-night, my soul, be still and sleep, God's heav'n will com - fort

on God's deep,—   God's deep, not thine, Be still and sleep.
tempest's sweep,—   God's hand, not thine, Be still and sleep.
night hours creep,— God's love, not thine, Be still and sleep.
those who weep,—   God's heav'n and thine, Be still and sleep.

104. THOUGH YOUR SINS BE AS SCARLET.

F. J. CROSBY.

W. H. DOANE.

DUET. *Gently.*

1. "Tho' your sins be as scar-let, They shall be as white as snow;
2. Hear the voice that en-treats you, Oh, re-turn ye un-to God!
3. He'll for-give your trans-gres-sions, And re-mem-ber them no more;

Tho' your sins be as scar-let, They shall be as white as snow;
Hear the voice that en-treats you, Oh, re-turn ye un-to God!
He'll for-give your trans-gres-sions, And re-mem-ber them no more;

QUARTET.

Tho' they be red . . . . . like crim-son, They shall be as wool!"
He is of great . . . . . . com-pas-sion, And of won-drous love;
"Look un-to Me . . . . . . - ye peo-ple," Saith the Lord your God;

Tho' they be red

DUET. *p*   QUARTET. *f*

"Tho' your sins be as scar-let, Tho' your sins be as scar-let,
Hear the voice that en-treats you, Hear the voice that en-treats you,
He'll for-give your transgres-sions, He'll for-give your transgressions,

p ritard.

They shall be as white as snow, They shall be as white as snow,"
Oh, re-turn ye un-to God! Oh, re-turn ye un-to God!
And re-mem-ber them no more, And re-mem-ber them no more.

E. E. HEWITT.　　　　　　　　　　　　　　　E. S. LORENZ.

1. Here peace, and love, and hope a-bide, Resting in my Sav-ior's arms;
2. He gen-tly whispers, "thou are mine," Resting in my Sav-ior's arms;
3. So let me pass thro' Ba-ca's vale, Resting in my Sav-ior's arms;
4. Oh, may I fall a-sleep at last, Resting in my Sav-ior's arms;

And com-forts flow, what-e'er be-tide, Resting in my Sav-ior's arms.
Faith glad-ly an-swers, I am thine, Resting in my Sav-ior's arms.
And find the springs that nev-er fail, Resting in my Sav-ior's arms.
Then, ev-'ry sin and sor-row past, Waking in my Sav-ior's arms.

CHORUS.

Rest - ing, rest - ing, Rest-ing in my

Rest-ing, rest-ing, I am sweet-ly rest-ing, I am rest-ing in my

Sav-ior's arms; Rest - ing,

Sav-ior's, Sav-ior's arms; I am rest-ing, sweet-ly rest-ing,

rest - ing,

rest-ing, sweet-ly rest-ing, Rest-ing in my Sav-ior's arms.

106. O IT WILL BE BRIGHTER TO-MORROW.

L. B. M.

L. BRIGGS MITCHELL.

1. O it will be bright-er to-mor-row, The Fa-ther is lov-ing and kind; The hope that he giv-eth in sor-row The trust-ing ones ev-er shall find.

2. O it will be bright-er to-mor-row, The earth-life is full of sad care; But e'en in its toil we may bor-row The joy that a-wait-eth us there.

3. O it will be bright-er to-mor-row, Go on in the hope from a-bove; And bur-y each heart ache and sor-row In in-fi-nite mer-cy and love.

CHORUS.

O it will be bright-er to-mor-row, The clouds that now darken the way Will van-ish with all of thy sor-row When dawneth the beautiful day.

107. 'TIS THE SAVIOR SPEAKS.

ADA BLENKHORN.

DR. S. B. JACKSON.

1. When the storm-toss'd waves are roll-ing, Wild a-cross the an-gry sea,
2. When my eyes are dim with weep-ing, And the way I can-not see,—
3. When beneath his smile of bless-ing, Clouds disperse and shad-ows flee,

Comes the voice their wrath con-trol-ling,—'Tis the Sav-ior speaks to me.
"Fear thou not; thy steps I'm keep-ing," Then my Sav-ior speaks to me.
Per-fect peace I am pos-sess-ing, For my Sav-ior speaks to me.

CHORUS.

'Tis the Sav - ior, bless-ed Sav - ior, 'Tis the
'Tis the Sav-ior speaks to me, 'Tis the Sav-ior speaks to me, 'Tis the

Sav - - - ior speaks to me, ... Words of
Sav-ior speaks to me, So sweet-ly speaks to me, Words of

mer - cy di-vine to cheer me, 'Tis the Saviour speaks to me.
love, divinely sweet, Words of love, and hope, and peace,

108. PASS IT ON.

JULIA H. JOHNSTON.

E. S. LORENZ.

1. Has some one shown you kindness? Pass it on, pass it on.
2. Has some one been for-giv-ing? Pass it on, pass it on.
3. All bless-ing is for shar-ing, Pass it on, pass it on.
4. You've heard good news of glad-ness, Pass it on, pass it on.

To hoard a joy is blind-ness, Pass it on, pass it on.
Has boun-ty crown'd your liv-ing? Pass it on, pass it on.
Be gen-'rous-ly un-spar-ing, Pass it on, pass it on.
To cheer the dark world's sad-ness, Pass it on, pass it on.

Think how much is done for you, Count your mer-cies, ev-er new;
Pleas-ant words and kind-ly deeds, These are what the whole world needs,
Ne'er sit down and i-dly grieve, O-ver loss you can't re-trieve;
Ti-dings glad, of peace, good will, All the world with joy should fill;

Some-thing is to oth-ers due, Pass it on, pass it on.
For such thought-ful care it pleads, Pass it on, pass it on.
Some-thing dai-ly you re-ceive, Pass it on, pass it on.
You who know the cure for ill, Pass it on, pass it on.

PASS IT ON. Concluded.

CHORUS.

Pass it on, ... each bless-ing keen-er joy will give, Pass it
Pass it on,

on, ... it is the tru-est life to live; Pass it on, ... since
Pass it on,
Pass it on,

Christ thy sinning doth forgive, Pass it on, pass it on.
Pass it on, pass it on.

109.

COME, CHILDREN, COME.

I. B.

I. BALTZELL.

1. To - day the Sav - ior calls, Come, chil - dren, come;
2. To - day the Sav - ior calls, Oh, lis - ten now!
3. To - day the Sav - ior calls; For ref - uge fly

Oh, ten - der, youth - ful souls, Why lon - ger roam?
With - in these sa - cred walls To Je - sus bow.
Be - fore his jus - tice falls; Come, death is nigh.

111

RESTING IN HOPE.

FANNY J. CROSBY.   ARTHUR W. NELSON.

DUET. *With great expression.*

1. I am rest-ing in hope, I am safe in His care, Whose mer-cy up-
2. I am rest-ing in hope, I am safe in His love, Now gone to pre-
3. I am rest-ing in hope and I will not re-pine, Thro' billows o'er-
4. I am rest-ing in hope, I am safe in his care, Whose promise as-

holds me, whose com-fort I share; I am rest-ing in hope of the
pare me a man-sion a-bove; I am rest-ing in hope of the
take me and storm may be mine; I am rest-ing in hope for my
sures me I soon shall be there; I am rest-ing in hope for I

joys that will come, When gathered with those who are call-ing me home.
song I shall sing, When anchored in glo-ry with Je-sus my King.
Sav-ior will come, And bear me a-way to the reap-ers at home.
know he is near, My sky is un-cloud-ed my faith-star is clear.

CHORUS.

Call-ing me home they are call-ing me home, I hear their glad

voi-ces be-yond the glad sea, Call-ing me home, yes,
Call-ing me

RESTING IN HOPE, Concluded.

call - ing me home, Voi - ces, glad voi - ces are call - ing for me.

call-ing me,

111.

ONLY ASK HIM!

E. R. LATTA.

GEO. E. MYERS.

1. Would you be a child of Je - sus? On - ly ask him!
2. Would you quit each earth - ly pleas-ure? On - ly ask him!
3. Would you feel the Sav - ior near you? On - ly ask him!
4. Would you be an heir of glo - ry? On - ly ask him!

For the love that nev - er ceas - es, On - ly ask him!
Would you lay up heav'n - ly treas-ure? On - ly ask him!
He'll ac - com - pa - ny and cheer you, On - ly ask him!
He will show the way be - fore you, On - ly ask him!

Ask in faith, his word be - liev-ing, Not the ho - ly Spir - it grieving;

And re - joice in the re - ceiv-ing! On - ly ask him!

113 R. of G. S R. N.

112. JESUS WILL ANSWER MY PRAYER!

E. E. HEWITT.

CHAS. K. LANGLEY.

Not too fast.

1. When a poor sin-ner I come to the throne, Jesus will answer my
2. When for the gift of his spir-it I pray, Jesus will answer my
3. Sometimes by ways that I can-not dis-cern, Jesus will answer my
4. Trust-ful-ly leav-ing with him my re-quest, Jesus will answer my

prayer! Pleading the blood that was shed to a-tone, Jesus will
prayer! Com-fort and guidance and keep-ing each day, Jesus will
prayer! Still at his feet bless-ed les-sons I learn, Jesus will
prayer! Some-how or oth-er he'll give what is best, Jesus will

CHORUS.

an-swer my prayer! Won-der-ful treasures of love, ...
Won-der-ful treasures of love,

Faith will bring down from a-bove: . . . . "Rich-es in glo-ry," on
from a-bove:

earth I may share, Je-sus will an-swer my prayer! . . .
will an-swer my prayer!

113. HARK TO THE CRYING!

V. G. RAMSEY.

WM. A. MAY.

1. { Oh, hark to the cry-ing! The na-tions are dy-ing, The nations of earth
   Oh, hark to the groaning: All na-ture is moaning; (*Omit.*

2. { There's a tree of God's planting, With leafage enchanting, That cures all earth's mad-
   And with pow'r super-nal, With pit - y e-ter-nal, (*Omit.* . . . . . .

3. { The na - tions are cry-ing, Yes, fall - ing and dy-ing! Oh, has - ten to tell
   Which grows by the riv - er, That floweth for-ev- er, (*Omit.* . . . . . .

in their fath-om-less woe!)
. . . .) Un - ceas-ing the an-guish, un-end-ing its flow.
ness, and blindness, and care ;
. . . .) He of - fers this balm for her pain and despair.
of the life - giv - ing tree,
. . . .) From the throne of God's mercy, abundant and free.

CHORUS.

{ Oh, haste where they langu<u>ish</u> In blindness and anguish, Soul-sick and soul -
{ And tell the glad sto-ry, Of par - don and glo-ry, Of (*Omit.* . . . .

hun-gry, in mad-ness and strife,
. . . .) healing and beau-ty, and full-ness of life.

115

114. CAN HE TRUST IN YOU?

MRS. LANTA WILSON SMITH.

E. S. LORENZ.

1. You have seen the hosts of Sa-tan marching to the fight,
2. There are foes that shun the bat-tle, but they strike a blow
3. There's a fort-ress to be guard-ed and the foe knows well
4. There are sol-diers that may nev-er en-ter thick-est fight,

With the ban-ner "Sin" a-bove them, they op-pose the right; But the
Un-der cov-er of the dark-ness, as the sen-tries know; So
There's a way to gain an en-trance if but one would tell; He will
There's an or-der that they cher-ish—"keep the ar-mor bright;" Nev-er

ar-my of Je-ho-vah keeps them all in view; If the
sen-ti-nels of Zi-on must be brave and true— If the
tempt and bribe and threat-en, ev-'ry art pur-sue— O the
wea-ry, ev-er faith-ful, hum-ble work they do, If the

Lord should want a soldier, can he trust in you? Can he trust in you.
Lord should want a watcher, can he trust in you? Can he trust in you,
Lord wants faithful servants, can he trust in you? Can he trust in you,
Lord should want a worker, can he trust in you? Can he trust in you,

CAN HE TRUST IN YOU? Concluded.

can he trust in you? If the Lord should want a soldier, can he trust in you?
can he trust in you? If the Lord should want a watcher, can he trust in you?
can he trust in you? O the Lord wants faithful servants, can he trust in you?
can he trust in you? If the Lord should want a worker, can he trust in you?

115. REST, WEARY PILGRIM.

MARIA STRAUB.

J. H. TENNEY.

Softly and slowly.

1. Rest, wea - ry pil - grim, thy jour - ney is o'er, Rest, sweet - ly
2. Nev - er a - gain shall thy storm - beat - en breast Sigh, deep - ly
3. Rest, wea - ry pil - grim, thy jour - ney is o'er, Rest, sweet - ly

rest, on the beau - ti - ful shore; Safe - ly at last thou hast
sigh, for the sweet "land of rest;" Gone to the Sav - ior's bright
rest, on the beau - ti - ful shore; Dan - gers and troub - les shall

Rit e dim.

reached the bright goal, Fa - - - ther - land, home of the soul.
Land of our Fa - ther, the light of the love.
man - sion a - bove, Rest (ev - er rest) in the light of his love.
harm thee no more, Rest (sweetly rest) on the beau - ti - ful shore.

116. IN THE SOLEMN DAY.

JENNIE WILSON.

W. A. OGDEN.

1. What will you do in the sol-emn day, That brings be-
reavement, grief and pain, When brightest hopes swift-ly fade a-way,
And earth-ly com-fort proves in vain? Can you lean on Christ? can you
trust the Friend Who in sor-rows gloom faith's glad light can blend?

2. What will you do in the sol-emn day, When death-shades
fall, and all a-lone Be-side the shad-ow-y sea you stray,
And cross its waves to shores unknown? Can you trust in Christ? can you
hold his hand, As you drift a-way from this bor-der-land?

3. What will you do in the sol-emn day, When you the
right-eous Judge shall meet? When earth and sea shall have fled a-way,
And God our Lord shall reign complete? Can you trust in Christ? and as
his be known, When the na-tions gath-er be-fore his throne?

REFRAIN.

In the sol-emn day that will surely come, When no human help a-vails,

IN THE SOLEMN DAY. Concluded.

Can you lean in faith on the arm di- vine Of the Friend that nev-er fails?

117.

SWEET HOSANNAS.

MRS. L. M. BUCK.

C. A. SHAW.

1. O why should not the children sing Their praise to him who made us free,
2. Sing of his love and tender care, That leads their young and wayward feet
3. Sing in a loud and joy - ful lay Our blest Redeemers worthy praise,

Till all their songs and service blend, With those be-side the crys- tal sea.
In ways of right and paths of peace, To liv-ing streams and pastures sweet.
And in their songs and triumphs share The glo-ries of his works and ways.

CHORUS.

Sing sweet ho- san - nas! Ming- ling love with loft - iest praise;

Sing sweet ho- san - nas, Till in heav'n the song we raise.

118.

A MIGHTY SAVIOR.

E. E. HEWITT.

E. S. LORENZ.

1. In pen - i - tence he brought me low, Then led me to the crim-son
2. He met my soul at Cal - va - ry, And o-pened there my eyes to
3. Such ten - der care hath he bestowed, He guides me on life's rug-ged
4. When all the scenes of time are past, My crown at his dear feet I'll

flow, . . . That cleanseth sinners white as snow. And there he freely sav'd me.
see . . . His ev - er-last-ing love for me, O there my Savior blessed me.
road; . . . His shoulder placed beneath my load, He dai-ly, hour-ly helps me.
cast, . . . And sing his grace from first to last, For Je-sus helps and saves me.

CHORUS.

'Tis a might-y, might-y Sav - ior I proclaim, praise his name! For he

saved me! For he saved me! 'Tis a might-y, mighty
saved me from my sin!   saved me from my sin!

love that keeps me still thro' ev-'ry ill, And it gives me peace with-in.

120

119. WHILE IT IS CALLED TO-DAY.

JENNIE WILSON.

J. H. ROSECRANS.

1. Swift-ly the night ap-proach-es, Fast glide the hours a-way;
2. Christ with thy soul is plead-ing, Free-ly his voice o-bey;
3. Trust in the Sav-ior's prom-ise, Nev-er will he be-tray;
4. Now is the time ac-cept-ed, Dan-ger is in de-lay;

Seek ye the life e-ter-nal, While it is called to-day.
Gain ye the great sal-va-tion, While it is called to-day.
Give un-to him thy ser-vice, While it is called to-day.
Ere it is night for-ev-er, Choose nev-er-end-ing day.

CHORUS.

While it is called to-day, . . . Turn not from Christ a-way;
While it is called, is called to-day, Turn not from Christ, from Christ a-way;

rit. e dim.

Mer-cy is of-fered on-ly While it is called to-day. . .
Mer-cy is of-fered of-fered on-ly While it is called, is called to-day.

120. WHAT SHALL I STAND BY?

Inscribed to my son, Earl.

REV. F. L. SNYDER. GEO. E. MEYERS.

Boldly.

1. What shall I stand by? a - mid the world-ly strife, What shall I
2. What shall I stand by? a - mid the earth-ly woe, What shall I
3. What shall I stand by? if men the truth as - sail, What shall I

stand by? a - mid the ills of life; When a-round me e - vil ris - eth
stand by? wher-ev - er I may go; When the car - nal pleasures have ob -
stand by? if e - vil would prevail; When a-round me gath - er shad-ows

up in all its might, Then comes the an - swer, Stand by the right.
scured the heav'nly light, Then comes the an - swer, Stand by the right.
of a com-ing night, Then comes the an - swer, Stand by the right.

CHORUS.

Stand by the right, stand by the right, Stand by the
Yes   Yes

right, firm - ly stand; In the world - ly striv - ings when but

WHAT SHALL I STAND BY? Concluded.

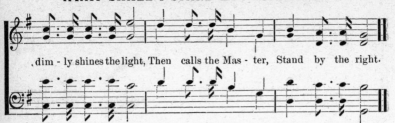

.dim - ly shines the light, Then calls the Mas - ter, Stand by the right.

121. LIVING LIKE THE LILIES.

WM. H. GARDNER.   WM. A. OGDEN.

Andante.

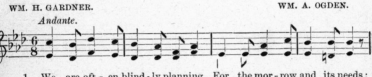

1. We are oft - en blind - ly planning, For the mor - row and its needs;
2. Oft - en do we rich - es cov - et, And the goal we al - most reach;
3. World-ly wis-dom, earth-ly glo-ry, Fill our hearts with fool-ish pride,
4. Live the pres - ent grandly, no-bly, Then in God's hand leave the rest;

S.   FINE.

But how ma - ny cas - tles crumble, As time on its mis-sion speeds.
But God takes our treasures from us, That he may some les - son teach.
And disgrace then comes up - on us, Till in shame our heads we hide.
And the mile-stones on life's journey Will by you be count - ed blest.

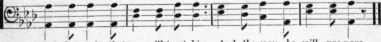

D.S.—*God but asks that we will trust him, And the way he will pre-pare.*

CHORUS.   D.S.

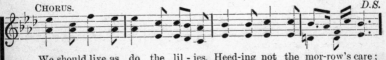

We should live as do the lil - ies, Heed-ing not the mor-row's care;

GO, WEARY ONE, GO.

W. H. D.

W. H. DOANE.

1. Poor child thou art wea-ry, Thy home is not here; O why wilt thou
2. Earth's pleasures have left thee, O, thou art de-ceived; Thy spir-it is
3. One look from thy Sav-ior, One smile of his love, One word of for-
4. He will not de-sert thee, Nor leave thee to pine; There rest on his

lan-guish When help is so near; Thou long-est for com-fort
wound-ed, Thy spir-it is grieved; The balm that would heal thee,
give-ness, Thy grief would re-move. He sees ev-'ry tear-drop,
bo-som, That rest may be thine. Sweet peace in be-liev-ing,

Earth cannot be-stow; Go, find it in Je-sus, Go, wea-ry one, go.
Friends cannot be-stow; Go, find it in Je-sus, Go, wea-ry one, go.
He feels for thy woe; Go, find it in Je-sus, Go, wea-ry one, go.
What rapture to know; Go, find it in Je-sus, Go, wea-ry one, go.

CHORUS.

Go to thy Sav-ior, he calls to-day; Lin-ger not, lin-ger not,

why de-lay; Go hum-bly to Je-sus, Go, wea-ry one, go.

123. SAVIOR, LISTEN WHILE WE SING.

GODFREY THRING.   J. A. PARKS.

1. Sav - ior, bless-ed Sav - ior, Lis - ten while we sing, Hearts and voi - ces
2. Brighter still and bright-er Glows the west-ern sun, Shed-ding all it's
3. Bliss, all bliss ex - cel - ling, When the ransom'd soul, Earth-ly toil for-

rais- ing, Prais- es to our King; All we have to of - fer, All we
glad-ness O'er our la - bor done; Time will soon be o - ver, Toil and
get- ting, Finds its promised goal; Where, in joy un - ending, Saints with

hope to be, Bod- y, soul, and spir - it, All we yield to thee.
sor- row past; May we, bless-ed Sav - ior, Find a home at last.
an- gels sing, Hearts and voi - ces rais - ing, Prais- es to their King.

CHORUS.
Bless — ed Sav - ior; All we bring to thee,.........

Bless - ed Sav - ior, Bless- ed Sav - ior, All we bring, we bring to thee,

Bod - y soul, and spir - it, All we have or hope to be, (to be.)

124.
COMING NOW.

JULIA H. JOHNSTON.

E. S. LORENZ.

1. In the ear - ly glow of the morn - ing - time, We are
2. In the fresh - est bloom of our buoy - ant youth, We are
3. He has bid us come, and his word is "Now," We are

com - ing, We are com - ing; Ere the
com - ing, We are com - ing; To the
com - ing, We are com - ing, We are com - ing; com - ing now; To the

bells of noon in the dis-tance chime, We are coming,- com-ing
Lord of love, and of life and truth, We are coming, com-ing
will of Christ we would gladly bow, We are coming, We are coming, com-ing

now, coming now. We are com-ing glad-ly to Je - sus Christ, Who has
now, coming now. And the ho - ly gift that to Christ we bring Is the
now, coming now. At the hour of pray'r, in the time of need, He will

of - fered free - ly a gift un-priced, Un-to him who for us was
low - ly heart that to him would cling, As be - fore the throne of the
bend to hear, he will bless in - deed, In his Name a - lone we will

COMING NOW. Concluded.

sac - ri - ficed, We are com-ing,   com-ing now, com-ing now.
Lord and King We are com-ing,   com-ing now, com-ing now.
hum - bly plead, We are com-ing, We are coming, com-ing now, com-ing now.

125.   JESUS, MY KING!

E. R. LATTA.   CHAS. K. LANGLEY.

1. Humbly to thee,   Je-sus, my King! I my poor heart trusting-ly bring!
2. I would by faith, Je-sus, my King! Ev-er to thee earn-est-ly cling!
3. I would to thee, Je-sus, my King! Car-ols of praise joy-ful-ly sing!
4. Thou art my all, Je-sus, my King! Thirsteth my soul? thou art the spring!

Thou didst for me   ful - ly a-tone; Make me, I pray, tru-ly thine own!
Whith-er - so - e'er on-ward I tend, Go with me, Lord, un - to the end!
Thou art my hope,   cru - cified Lamb! Come I to thee just as I am!
Wa - ter of life thou wilt be-stow,   If to the fount I will but go!

REFRAIN.

Je-sus, my King! Je-sus, my King! Je-sus, my Lord and my King, Lord and King!

Je - sus, my King! Je-sus, my King! Je-sus, my Lord and my King!

126. COUNTING FOR CHRIST.

G. W. HASKELL.

W. S. MARTIN.

1. Are you counting for the Mas-ter ev-'ry day? (ev'ry day?) Do you
2. Are you counting for the Mas-ter ev-'ry day? (ev'ry day?) Do you
3. Are you counting for the Mas-ter ev-'ry day? (ev'ry day?) Gaining

let the bless-ed Spir-it have his way? (have his way?) Do you stand for
seek his bless-ed pre-cepts to o - bey? (to o-bey?) And in all your
vic-to-ries for Je-sus in the fray? (in the fray?) Oh put on his

Christ the Lord? Are you trust-ing in his word? Oh, be counting for the
tho'ts or plans, Do you hon-or his com-mands? Oh, be counting for the
ar-mor bright, And be faith-ful in the fight, Oh, be counting for the

D. S.—*Are you counting for the*

FINE. CHORUS.

Master ev-'ry day. Are you count - - ing, count-ing, Are you
Are you counting for the Master?

Master ev-'ry day?

D.S.

counting for the Master ev'ry day? Are you count - - ing, counting,
Are you counting for the Master?

127. THE GOLDEN SUMMERLAND.

G. M. BILLS.   M. L. McPHAIL.

1. To the ha-ven of our dreams, Where the day e-ter-nal beams, And the
2. 'Mid the sigh-ing of the blast, We are watching from the mast, For the
3. When the clouds are hanging low, And we know not where to go, To our
4. When the breakers all are past, And their roar is hush'd at last, And we

tides of glad-ness wash a tear-less strand, We will spread a hope-ful
stars of truth that guide us to the land; And up-on the blending
aid will come a joy in-spir-ing hand; For our pi-lot can-not
hear the wel-come of the an-gel band, We will an-chor in the

D.S.—*For our souls can fear no*

sail To the ris-ing homeward gale, Ev-er long-ing for the
spray, Ev-er gleams a cheer-ing ray From love's bea-con in the
fail, At the rud-der or the sail, As he bears us to the
bay Nev-er-more to drift a-way From our moor-ings in the

ill From the ebb-ing of the tide, In the ha-ven of the

FINE.   CHORUS.

gold-en summer-land.   To the gold-en sum-mer-land, We will

gold-en sum-mer-land.   D.S.

sweet-ly, calm-ly glide, While the angels wave a wel-come on the strand.

R. of G. 9 R. N.

WONDROUS GRACE.

W. S. MARTIN.

J. H. TENNEY.

1. Wondrous grace that reaches me, Sin-ful tho' my heart may be (may be;)
2. Grace to keep me day by day, Grace to help me all the way (the way;)
3. Wondrous grace and mighty love, This the theme of saints a-bove (above,)

Per-fect cleans-ing here is giv'n, Fit-ting me for joys of heav'n. (of heav'n.)
Sat-is-fied my soul can be, With this grace and love so free. (so free.)
Who are gaz-ing on the face Of the Lord, who saved by grace. (by grace.)

CHORUS.

Wondrous grace, . . the wondrous grace, . . I will tell . . . . in
Wondrous grace, the wondrous grace, I will tell

ev-'ry place; . . . Grace that saves . . . me from my
in ev-'ry place; Grace that saves me

sin, . . . Grace that makes . me pure with-in . . . .
from my sin, Grace that makes me pure with-in.

129. AT THE FEET OF MY SAVIOR.

REV. JOHNSON OATMAN, JR.

CHAS. H. GABRIEL.

1. Once I found a balm for my wound-ed soul, When I
2. When I'm tem-pest tossed on life's storm-y deep, Then I
3. Praise his ho-ly name! un-til life is past I will

knelt at the feet of my Sav-ior; The Phy-si-cian then made my
kneel at the feet of my Sav-ior; And I find the storm quickly
kneel at the feet of my Sav-ior; Then a crown of life he will

poor heart whole, When I knelt at the feet of my Sav-ior.
hushed to sleep, As I kneel at the feet of my Sav-ior.
grant at last, While I kneel at the feet of my Sav-ior.

Chorus.

{ O what joy I find, O what peace of mind, When I
{ For he bids me rest on his lov-ing breast, When I

1 kneel at the feet of my Sav-ior; **2** kneel at the feet of my Sav-ior.

130. ASHAMED OF JESUS.

JOSEPH GRIGG.   W. A. OGDEN.

1. Je - sus, and shall it ev - er be, A mortal man a-shamed of thee?
2. A-shamed of Je - sus! that dear Friend On whom our hopes of heav'n depend!
3. A-shamed of Je - sus! yes, I may, When I've no guilt to wash a - way;
4. Till then—nor is my trust-ing vain—Till then I boast a Sav-ior slain!

Ashamed of thee, whom an-gels praise, Whose glories shine thro' endless days?
No; when I blush, be this my shame, That I no more re - vere his name.
No tear to wipe, no good to crave, No fears to quell, no soul to save.
And O, may this my glo - ry be, That Christ is not ashamed of sin.

REFRAIN.

Ashamed of Je - sus sooner far, ...
Ashamed of Je - sus soon-er far, oh, soon-er far,

Let eve - ning blush . . . . . to own a star; . . . . . .
Let eve-ning blush to own a star, to own a star;

He sheds the beams . . . . of light di - vine, ...
He sheds the beams of light di-vine,

ASHAMED OF JESUS. Concluded.

D.C. *Last stanza.*

O'er this be-night-ed soul, this soul of mine. A-men.

131. ## ALL IS WELL.

E. E. HEWITT.

J. H. TENNEY.

1. Since e-ter-nal life is mine, All is well, all is well;
2. Thro' the shift-ing scenes of time, All is well, all is well;
3. Work-ing out my high-est good, All is well, all is well;
   All is well, All is well;

'Round the cross my hopes en-twine, All is well, all is well.
In my heart the joy-bells chime, All is well, all is well.
Though not al-ways un-der-stood, All is well, all is well.
All is well, All is well.

Je-sus bore the cross for me, Je-sus died to set me free,
Summer's sun and win-ter's snow, Shall my Fa-ther's goodness show;
Af-ter con-flict, af-ter pain, In the home of joy's bright reign,

I am now at lib-er-ty, All is well, All is well.
Peace shall like a riv-er flow, All is well, All is well.
Christ the mean-ing will ex-plain, All is well, All is well.
All is well, All is well.

132.
STARS IN MY CROWN.

E. D. MUND.
SOLO.

E. S. LORENZ.

1. I have found a dear Sav-ior, a Friend, and a Guide, Who has
2. Shall I self-ish-ly walk in the heav-en-ly way That will
3. Do thou aid me, dear Lord, to de-vote ev-'ry power To the

freed me from shackles that bound me; Do I wish all a-lone in his
lead me to joys all im-mor-tal; While the friend at my side still in
lead-ing of souls un-to Je-sus; That with me they may join in that

love to con-fide, Ne'er to lead to him friends that surround me?
darkness doth stray? Shall I leave him to miss heav-en's por-tal?
rapt-ur-ous hour, Sing-ing praise to the Sav-ior that frees us.

CHORUS.

Will there be stars in my crown? Stars in my crown? Will there be

stars in my crown of re-joic-ing? Will not Heav'n be more sweet,

When our friends we can greet, As the stars in our crown of re- joic- ing?

133. A BANNER FOR JESUS.

E. E. HEWITT.   ADAM GEIBEL.

1. Tell the good news of the kingdom, Tell it wher-ev - er you go,
2. Go to the sad and dis-couraged, Tell-ing the wea-ry of rest;
3. Go to the cold and in-dif-ferent, Fear not, tho' trembling and weak:
4. Spreading the glad in - vi - ta - tion, Ech- o the life giv-ing call,

Hold up a ban - ner for Je - sus, Show it to friend and to foe.
Tell - ing the pre - cious sal - va - tion, Ask them to come and be blest.
Go in the might of the Spir - it He will give strength to the weak.
Tell of his grace, all suf - fi - cient, Par - don and heal - ing for all.

CHORUS.

Hold up the ban - ner, Giv- en to us to dis - play,
Hold up the banner, hold up the banner,

Won- der- ful, blood-sprinkled banner, Wave it for Je - sus to-day.

134. JESUS CAME TO ME.

FLORA BEST HARRIS.

CHAS. H. GABRIEL.

1. A-cross the wa-ters far-ing, The night on land and sea,
   I had no Guide or Pi-lot, 'Till Je-sus came to me.
   He came, the "Man of sor-rows," The man of vic-to-ry,

2. O soul in tem-pest toss-ing, 'Tis Christ of Gal-i-lee,
   Be-loved as God's an-oint-ed, The Lord of shore and sea.
   He died, but he is ris-en, Seek not a-mong the dead;

3. He walks the dark-'ning wa-ters, And leaves a shin-ing way,
   This Sav-ior of all sav-ior's, Let him on board, I pray;
   What mat-ters storm or mid-night, He comes, he comes to thee,

D.S.—And dawn a-rose from dark-ness, And peace was on the sea.
D.S.—To-day the tem-pest knows him, The bil-lows feel his tread.
D.S.—I know him in his beau-ty, For Je-sus came to me.

REFRAIN.

He came, .. he came to me, He came, .. he came to me.
He came to me, ...   He came to me. ...

135. WITH JESUS ON BOARD.

E. E. HEWITT.   E. S. LORENZ.

1. We're rounding the cape, the Cape of Good Hope; Un - furl ev - 'ry
2. Our trust is in him who's a - ble to save, He rides on the
3. The ban - ner of love is float - ing o'er-head, Our chart is the

sail, and strengthen each rope; We're bounding a - way a - cross the white foam,
cloud, he walks on the wave; The word that spake "peace" on wild Gal - i - lee
Book that nev - er mis-led; All praise to his grace, we'll sing ev - er-more,

CHORUS.

And soon we shall be with Je - sus at home.) A - way! . . . . .
Will pil - ot us still on life's toss-ing sea. } A - way! a-way! with
We'll make a good voy - age to E-den's bright shore.)

. . . . A - way! . . . . Tho' tempests may
Je - sus on board, The waves o - bey the voice of the Lord ;

blow, tho' breakers may roar, We'll soon be at home on the beau-ti - ful shore.

136.
FALL INTO LINE.

L. E. J.

L. E. JONES.

1. There is need of val-iant sol-diers in the cause of right, For the
2. There is need of val-iant sol-diers standing firm and true, Who will
3. There is need of val-iant sol-diers who will march to - day, At the

en - e - my is strong; Yet with Je - sus Christ, our Captain, we shall
stem the rum fiend's pow'r; In the res - cue of the cap-tive there is
Lead-er's blest com - mand; Who will meet the gi - ant e - vil and op -

CHORUS.

win the fight 'Gainst the gath - ered hosts of wrong.
much to do, So em - ploy each fleet - ing hour. } Fall in - to
pose its sway, O - ver all our na - tive land.

line,   Fall in- to line,   Join the ar-my of the King,
Fall in- to line,   fall in- to line,

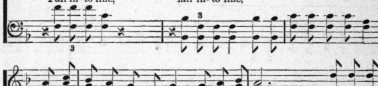

Seek some oth - er heart to bring ; Fall in - to line,   fall in - to
Fall in - to line,

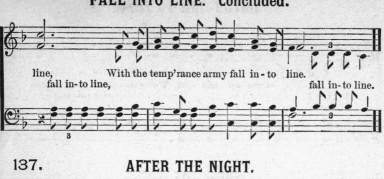

line,
fall in-to line,
With the temp'rance army fall in - to line.
fall in-to line.

137. AFTER THE NIGHT.

FUNERAL QUARTET.

JENNIE WILSON.

E. S. LORENZ.

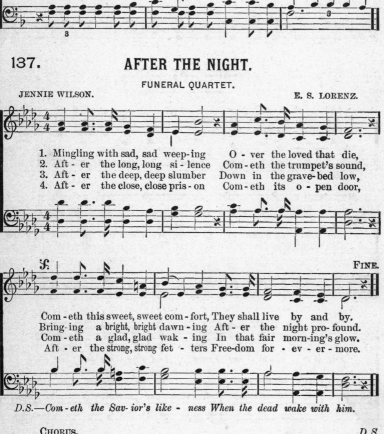

1. Mingling with sad, sad weep-ing   O - ver the loved that die,
2. Aft - er the long, long si - lence   Com- eth the trumpet's sound,
3. Aft - er the deep, deep slumber   Down in the grave-bed low,
4. Aft - er the close, close pris - on   Com- eth its o - pen door,

Com - eth this sweet, sweet com - fort, They shall live   by and by.
Bring-ing a bright, bright dawn - ing Aft - er the night pro- found.
Com - eth a glad, glad wak - ing In that fair morn-ing's glow.
Aft - er the strong, strong fet - ters Free-dom for - ev - er-more.

D.S.—Com - eth the Sav - ior's like - ness When the dead wake with him.

CHORUS.

D. S.

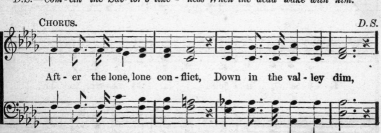

Aft - er the lone, lone con - flict,   Down in the val - ley dim,

138.   RETURNING TO ZION.

PRICILLA J. OWENS.   W. A. OGDEN.

1. The bat-tles now are end-ed, We've won the vic-t'ry splen-did,
2. Re-turn-ing home to Zi-on, We've done with pain and sigh-ing,
3. The bat-tles all are end-ed, The cause so long de-fend-ed

And march in glad ar-ray, .. And march in glad ar-ray;
No foes our peace de-stroy, No foes our peace de-stroy;
For-ev-er now is won, For-ev-er now is won;

Re-turn-ing home to Zi-on, We cheer for Ju-dah's Li-on,
No march o'er des-erts wea-ry, No camp in trench-es drear-y,
We tell the conquering sto-ry, And al-ways give the glo-ry

And sing up-on our way, And sing up-on our way.
But ev-er-last-ing joy, But ev-er-last-ing joy.
To God's be-lov-ed Son, To God's be-lov-ed Son.

CHORUS.

Re-joice! ., re-joice! .. O glad re-turn-ing home! ..
Re-joice!   re-joice!   re-joice!

Copyright, 1897, by E. S. Lorenz.

140

RETURNING TO ZION. Concluded.

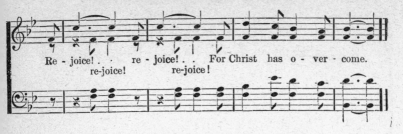

Re - joice! . . re - joice! . . For Christ has o - ver - come.
re-joice!   re-joice!

---

139. WITH SONGS OF HARVEST HOME.

F. S. SHEPARD.   E. S. LORENZ.
Allegretto.

1. The garner'd sheaves we're bring - ing, The praise of God we're sing - ing;
2. The seed was sown with weep - ing, But joy - ous was the reap - ing,
3. The serv - ice brought a bless - ing, Far, far be - yond ex - press - ing;

The courts of heav'n are ring - ing With songs of har - vest home.
And now our hearts are leap - ing With songs of har - vest home.
We come, our love con - fess - ing, With songs of har - vest home.

CHORUS.

With songs (With songs) of harvest home, Blest songs (Blest songs) of harvest home,

Our sheaves we bring be - fore our King, With songs of har - vest home.

140.
RISE, AND LET ME IN!

A. C. COXE, ARR.   W. A. OGDEN.

1. In the si-lent mid-night watch-es, List . . . . . thy
   List thy bosom's door,
2. Death comes down with reckless foot-steps To . . . . . the
   To the hall and hut,
3. Then, how vain to stand en-treat-ing Christ . . . . . to
   Christ to let you in,

bosom's door! . . . . . . How it knock-eth, knocketh, knocketh,
   list thy bosom's door!
hall and hut, ... Think you death will tar-ry knock-ing
   to the hall and hut;
let thee in . . . . At the door of heav-en beat-ing,
   Christ to let thee in.

Knock - - - eth ev - er - more . . . . . .
Knocketh ev - er - more, knocketh ev - er - more.
When . . . . . the door is shut? . . . . .
When the door is shut, when the door is shut?
Wail - - ing for thy sin . . . .
Wail-ing for thy sin, wail-ing for thy sin.

Say not 'tis thy pul-ses beat-ing; Heart oppressed by sin!
Je-sus wait-eth, wait-eth, wait-eth; But the door is fast!
Nay, a-las, too late thy plead-ing, Hast thou then for-got?

RISE, AND LET ME IN. Concluded.

'Tis thy Sav-ior knocks and cri - eth, Rise, and let me in!
Grieved a - way the Sav-ior go - eth, Death comes in at last!
Je - sus wait-ed long to know thee, Now he knows thee not!

CHORUS.

"Rise, ... and let me in, ... Rise, and let me
"Rise, and let me in! rise, and let me in!

in." Still the loving Savior knocks and crieth, "Rise, and let me in!"

141. HOLD THOU MY HANDS.

E. S. LORENZ.

1. Hold thou my hands! Hold thou my hands! In grief and joy, in hope and fear,
2. If e'er by doubts If e'er by doubts Of thy good Father-hood depressed,
3. Hold thou my hands—Hold thou my hands—These passionate hands too quick to smite,
4. And when at length, And when at length, With darkened eyes and fingers cold,

Lord, let me feel that thou art near; Hold thou my hands! Hold thou my hands!
I can - not find in thee my rest, Hold thou my hands! Hold thou my hands!
These hands so eag-er for de-light; Hold thou my hands! Hold thou my hands!
I seek some last loved hand to hold, Hold thou my hands! Hold thou my hands!

143

142. WATCH YOUR WORDS.

MRS. M. M. N.   MRS. M. M. NEWTON.

1. Watch your words: like the flow'rs, some are fair, pure and sweet, Some are like nox-ious
2. Watch your words, they have pow'r, they may com-fort and bless, They may soothe, they may
3. Watch your words, they may prove stepping stones to suc-cess, Or may turn to stern

weeds which we oft dread to meet; Some are like the bright sunshine, some
heal, they may cheer and ca-ress; Like the fire they may burn, like the
bar-riers as on-ward you press; They may help some poor brother a-

like the dark cloud; Like the zeph-yr or blast, some are soft, some loud.
frost, they may chill, Like the rain they may fall for our good or ill.
long life's high-way, Or may crush out the hope that has been his stay.

REFRAIN.

Watch your words,   watch your words,   Watch your
They have pow'r,   ev-'ry hour,

words, watch your words to-day!   Watch your words, ...
to-day, Watch your words, speak the truth,

144

Watch your words, ... Watch your words, watch your words al - way.
Watch your words, in your youth,

143. ## HEAR THE LOVING VOICE.

J. W. KOUNSE, ALT.
DUET.

J. H. TENNEY.

1. Hear the lov - ing voice of Je - sus Say - ing kind - ly un - to all,
2. Give to Je - sus faithful la - bor, Sow the pre - cious seed di - vine;
3. We must ev - er toil for Je - sus, And a - long the a - ges dim,

"In my vine - yard go and la - bor," And o - bey the earn - est call.
And the fruit - age of the har - vest Shall re - joice that heart of thine.
An - gel hands will reap the fruit - age, Gath'ring up the fruit for him.

CHORUS.

Work for Je - sus in his vine - yard While the morn - ing sun is bright;

For the day will soon be end - ed, Soon will fall the shades of night.

R. of G. 10 R. N.

WE'LL MEET AGAIN.

MRS. E. W. CHAPMAN.   J. H. TENNEY.

1. Farewell, we now . . . . . . a - gain must part, ...
2. Farewell, we say . . . . . . with ten- der tone, ...
3. Farewell! sweet hope . . . . . . with us shall dwell, ...

1. Farewell, we now   a- gain must part,
2. Farewell, we say   with ten- der tone,
3. Farewell! sweet hope   with us shall dwell,

The hours have quick - ly passed a - way, ...
Far lies the fu - ture veiled from sight, ...
And trav- 'ling on life's peace - ful road, ...

have quick - ly passed a - way,
the fu - ture veiled from sight,
on life's peace- ful road,

But cherished in . . . . . . each lov - ing heart, ...
But when we meet . . . . . . be - side the throne, ...
With grat - i - tude . . . . . . our hearts shall swell . . . . .

But cherished in   each lov - ing heart
But when we meet   be-side the throne
With grat - i - tude   our hearts shall swell,

Dwell mem - 'ries of this hap - py day.
We'll know all things were or - dered right. . . . . .
That we shall meet in heav'n with God.

Dwell mem - 'ries of this day, this hap - py day. . . . . .
We'll know all things, all things were or-dered right. . . . .
That we shall meet, shall meet in heav'n with God. . . . .

CHORUS.

We'll meet a-gain . . . . . We'll meet a-gain, ...

We'll meet a-gain,   We'll meet a-gain,

We'll meet, . . . yes, meet a - gain, ...

We'll meet a-gain, yes, meet a-gain, we'll meet a-gain,

If not with-in . . . . . . these halls we love, ...

If not with-in   these halls we love,

In yon-der shin - - - ing courts a-bove, ...

In yon-der shin-ing courts a-bove, in courts above,

In heav'n we'll meet a-gain. . . . .

In heav'n we'll meet a-gain, we'll meet a-gain. . . . .

145. THE SUN IS SHINING STILL.

SOLO AND MALE CHORUS.

REV. H. J. ZELLEY.

E. S. LORENZ.

1. The clouds that gath-er dark and drear   Bright sil - ver lin-ings
2. I find it so a-mid life's cares,   That press my spir - it
3. The wea - ry hours of day may be   Like shades of dark-est
4. Some-time the gloom will be dispelled,   The shad - ows flee a-

wear;   Be - cause, just on the oth - er side,   The
sore,   It's al - ways light be - hind the clouds,   Though
night;   But soon the sun will pierce the clouds,   At
way;   And all the dark - est shades of night   Give

sun   is shin - ing   clear.
oft - en dark   be - fore.
eve - ning 'twill be   light.
place to end - less   day.

CHORUS.

Be - hind the clouds   the
Be - hind, be - hind the clouds the

THE SUN IS SHINING STILL. Concluded.

sun shines clear,   Then   why should we   give place to
sun, the sun shines clear, Then   why, then why should we   give

doubt or fear?   O   let your heart   this message thrill,
place to doubt or fear? O   let your fainting heart this cheering message thrill,

Slower.   *Rit.*

Tho' dark and drear the clouds ap-pear, The   sun   is   shin-ing still.

146.   WE'LL HELP THE CAUSE ALONG.

JOSEPHINE POLLARD.   W. H. DOANE.

FINE.

1. { We must work and pray to-geth - er, Work-ing, pray-ing for the right; }
   { We must work a-gainst the   e - vil, Till   we con-quer by our might. }

2. { In de-fense of truth and jus - tice, Like a bul-wark we must stand, }
   { And the soul that's full of cour - age Will give cour-age to the hand. }

D.C.—U - nit - ed thus in strength and pray'r, We'll help the cause a - long.

CHORUS.   D.C.

We're strong to do, we're strong to dare, In   faith and hope we're strong;

3 We must work and not be weary, | 4 Hark! the crystal streams and fountains,
Though we conquer not to-day; | Swell the chorus of our song;
For the rescue of our brothers, | And they seem to be rejoicing
We must work as well as pray. | As they help the cause along.

149

147. THE BATTLE-FLAG OF JESUS.

E. R. LATTA. CHAS. K. LANGLEY.

In martial spirit.

1. A - way to the bat - tle, Up - on the Savior's ground! Away to the
2. A - way to the bat - tle, As oth - ers march along! A - way to the
3. A - way to the bat - tle! For Je - sus, vol - un - teer! A - way to the

bat - tle, O hear the trum - pet sound!
bat - tle, With Gid - eon shout and song!
bat - tle, Nor yield to doubt or fear!

DUET.

Up with the flag— the
Up with the flag— the
Up with the flag that

ALL.

bat - tle-flag, so dear! Yes, up with the bat - tle-flag of Je - sus!
bat - tle-flag we love! Yes, up with the bat - tle-flag of Je - sus!
leads to vic - to - ry! Yes, up with the bat - tle-flag of Je - sus!

DUET.

Up with the flag—the bat - tle-flag, so dear!
Up with the flag—the bat - tle- flag, we love! } Yes, up with the
Up with the flag that leads to vic - to - ry!

ALL.

battle-flag of Je - sus! A - way to the battle, The foe, bravely meeting!

CHORUS.

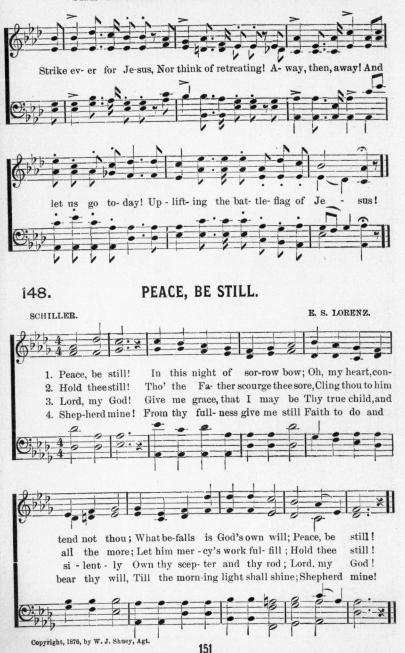

THE BATTLE-FLAG OF JESUS. Concluded.

Strike ev- er for Je-sus, Nor think of retreating! A-way, then, away! And let us go to-day! Up-lift-ing the bat-tle-flag of Je- sus!

148. PEACE, BE STILL.

SCHILLER.   E. S. LORENZ.

1. Peace, be still! In this night of sor-row bow; Oh, my heart, con-
2. Hold thee still! Tho' the Fa- ther scourge thee sore, Cling thou to him
3. Lord, my God! Give me grace, that I may be Thy true child, and
4. Shep-herd mine! From thy full- ness give me still Faith to do and

tend not thou; What be-falls is God's own will; Peace, be   still!
all the more; Let him mer -cy's work ful- fill ; Hold thee   still!
si - lent- ly Own thy scep- ter and thy rod ; Lord, my   God!
bear thy will, Till the morn-ing light shall shine;Shepherd   mine!

149. IN THE HOLLOW OF HIS HAND.

IDA SCOTT TAYLOR.

ADAM GEIBEL.

1. I've a ten-der lov-ing Friend Whom I can-not com-prehend, In his
2. Not a place where I may go, Not a tho't that I may know, But are
3. I will trust him with my all, I will an-swer to his call, And will

ma-jes-ty and wis-dom, deep and grand; But I know his love is
or-dered by his wis-dom and con-trol, Not a troub-le or dis-
hast-en to o-bey his blest com-mand; I will nev-er doubt or

D. S.—In the dark and drear-y

true, And what-ev-er I may do, He will hold me in the
tress That he will not own and bless, For he sym-pa-thi-zes
fear While my Lord and King is near, He will hold me in the

hour, When I feel the temp-ter's pow'r, He will hold me in the

FINE. CHORUS. hold me safe-ly

hol-low of his hand.
sweet-ly with my soul. } He will hold me, safe-ly hold me,
hol-low of his hand.

hol-low of his hand.

IN THE HOLLOW OF HIS HAND. Concluded.

hold me,

D.S.

hold me in his hand, Oh such love as his I can-not un-der-stand!

150. NOW IS THE TIME.

MRS. H. E. JONES.

CHAS. H. GABRIEL.

1. Now is the time to la - bor, Now is the time to climb; We
2. *Now* is the time for sow - ing, En - ter the fer - tile fields To
3. Now is the time to la - bor; Let us, then, watch and pray; For,
4. Now is the time to gath - er Treas-ures a - long the way; To

on - ly can boast of the *now*, my friends, So let us improve the time.
scat- ter some seeds by our no-ble deeds—'Twill bring us a goodly yield.
ver - i - ly, soon we shall reach life's noon, And rush to the twi- light gray.
seek out the gems for our di - a-dems, To shine thro' an endless day.

CHORUS.

Let . . . . us im-prove the *now*, Let us be faith-ful now!
Let us im-prove the *now*, my friends,

For la - bor begun with the rising sun Will lift to the mountain's brow.

153

151. TELL THE STORY.

F. S. S.

F. S. SHEPARD.

1. There's a sto-ry oft re-peat-ed, true and old, Sto-ry pre-cious more than an-y ev-er told; 'Tis of Jesus' wondrous love, Which his death doth ful-ly prove, Love that would the err-ing ev-'ry where en-fold.

2. Oh! the Sav-ior's love is won-der-ful to see, And it know-eth neith-er lim-it or de-gree; 'Neath its shadow there is peace, There all wea-ry striv-ings cease, There the slaves of sin's dread bondage are set free.

3. Tell, oh! tell this bless-ed sto-ry far and near, That the wea-ry, heav-y-ladened ones may hear, For in Je-sus all may rest, All who come to him are bless'd, Sin and care and doubt with him all dis-ap-pear.

CHORUS.

Tell the sto - - ry full and free, Tell the sto - - ry full and free;
won-der-ful sto - ry won-der-ful sto-ry full and free;

TELL THE STORY. Concluded.

Tell the won - drous sto - ry of Je - sus' love,

Tell the wondrous, wondrous sto - ry of Je - sus' mighty love,

Tell the won - drous sto - ry of Je - sus' love,

Tell the sto - - ry full and free, full and free.

won-der-ful sto - ry

152. A REST REMAINS.
(GEER.)

CHARLES WESLEY.   GREATOREX COLLECTION.

1. Lord, I be-lieve a rest re-mains, To all thy peo - ple known;
2. A rest where all our soul's de -sire Is fixed on things a - bove;
3. O, that I now that rest might know, Be-lieve, and en - ter in!
4. Re - move all hard - ness from my heart; All un - be - lief re - move;

A rest where pure en - joy-ment reigns, And thou art loved a - lone ;—
Where fear, and sin, and grief ex - pire, Cast out by per - fect love.
Now, Sav - iour, now the pow'r be - stow, And let me cease from sin.
To me the rest of faith im - part, The Sab-bath of thy love.

155

153. BLESSED DAY AND HOUR.

LOUISA E. LITZSINGER.　　　　　　　　　WM. A. MAY.

1. 2. 3. O, bless - ed day! O, hap - py hour!
O, bless - ed day! O, hap - py hour!

When first the Ho - ly Spir-it's pow'r Convinced my soul of sin;
When love and grace with ho - ly pow'r Re-vealed the Sav - ior's charm,
Child of the Fa - ther now am I An heir to Christ's es - tate!

When first I o - pened wide the door Whose bolts had oft re -
In Je - sus Christ, my soul has won Free ac - cess to the
Clothed in his robe of right - eous-ness, My soul shall pass in

poco rit.

fused be-fore To let the Sav-ior in, To let the Sav-ior in.
Father's throne Where I am safe from harm, Where I am safe from harm!
per - fect dress Thro' heaven's pear-ly gate, Thro' heav-en's pear-ly gate!

REFRAIN. *tempo.*

O, bless - ed day! O, hap - py hour!
O, bless - ed day, O. hap - py hour!

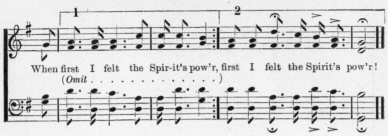

When first I felt the Spir-it's pow'r, first I felt the Spirit's pow'r!
(Omit . . . .)

154.   NEVER ALONE.

MRS. FRANK A. BRECK.   E. S. LORENZ.

Slowly.

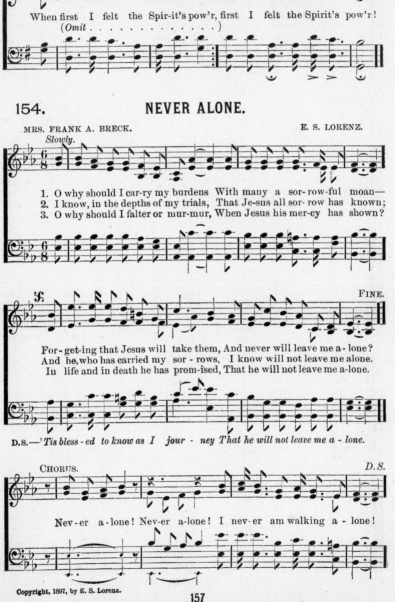

1. O why should I car-ry my burdens With many a sor-row-ful moan—
2. I know, in the depths of my trials, That Je-sus all sor-row has known;
3. O why should I falter or mur-mur, When Jesus his mer-cy has shown?

FINE.

For-get-ing that Jesus will take them, And never will leave me a-lone?
And he, who has carried my sor-rows, I know will not leave me alone.
In life and in death he has prom-ised, That he will not leave me a-lone.

D.S.—'Tis bless-ed to know as I jour-ney That he will not leave me a-lone.

CHORUS.   D.S.

Nev-er a-lone! Nev-er a-lone! I nev-er am walking a-lone!

155.
CARING FOR ME.

E. E. HEWITT.

CHAS. H. GABRIEL.

1. I'm trust-ing to-day in the word of the Lord, I know he is
2. Tho' clouds o-ver-shad-ow the ra-diant blue sky, I know he is
3. Then on-ward I press with a song in my heart, I know he is

car-ing for me; His prom-ise will ev-er sweet comfort af-ford,
car-ing for me; The sun of his love is still shin-ing on high,
car-ing for me; His good-ness and mer-cy will nev-er de-part,

I know he is car-ing for me. On him, my dear
I know he is car-ing for me. In mo-ments of
I know he is car-ing for me. I'll cling to the

Sav-ior, I cast ev-'ry care, His shoulders all-might-y my
dark-ness, his cross I em-brace, He cheers ev-'ry night with the
hand that on Cal-va-ry bled, And on his kind bo-som will

bur-dens will bear, In ten-der com-pas-sion, my sor-row he'll share,
lamp of his grace, And soon I shall see the full light of his face,
pil-low my head; With faith in his love, in his foot-steps I'll tread,

CARING FOR ME. Concluded.

REFRAIN.

I know he is car-ing for me.
Car - - ing for
Car-ing, I know he is
me, ... car - - ing for me, ... I'm trusting to-
car-ing for me, Car-ing, I know he is car-ing for me,
day in the word of the Lord, I know he is car-ing for me.

156. PRAISE THE LORD.

JOHN KEMPTHORNE.   C. M. VON WEBER, 1820.

1. Praise the Lord; ye heav'ns a - dore him; Praise him, angels, in the height;
2. Praise the Lord, for he hath spo - ken; Worlds his mighty voice obeyed:
3. Praise the Lord, for he is glo-rious; Nev-er shall his prom-ise fail;
4. Praise the God of our sal - va - tion, Hosts on high his pow'r proclaim;

Sun and moon, re - joice be- fore him; Praise him all ye stars of light.
Laws, which nev- er can be bro - ken, For their guidance he hath made.
God hath made his saints vic- to - rious, Sin and death shall not pre- vail.
Heav'n and earth, and all cre - a - tion, Praise and mag-ni - fy his name.

157. NOT LONG.

M. M. N.

MRS. MARTHA MILLS NEWTON.

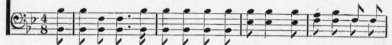

1. Not long, not long these painful sep - a - ra-tions, When those we love are
2. Not long, not long must these frail bodies suf-fer, How quickly snaps the
3. Not far, not far   is heav'n to those who serve Him, On wings of love the

bu - ried from our sight; 'Twill not be long un - til we go to
brit - tle thread of   life; Earth's cords are sev - ered, ten - der - est ties
eag - er spir - it flies, And welcomed by   de - part - ed friends and

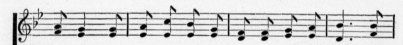

join them, To dwell for - ev - er   in the realms of light. How
are riven—Ces - sa - tion from the   spir - it's stub - born strife. 'Twill
kin - dred, Glides in - to gold - en gates of par - a - dise. So

sweet 'twill be when freed from im - per - fec - tion, Where loved ones now are
not be long, for soon this life is end - ed, Al-though we live thro'-
let us live that when we hear death's summons, We'll be prepared with-

NOT LONG. Concluded.

safe - ly gath-ered home, Where doubt, dis- may, heart-breaking dis - ap -
out th' al - lot - ted span; Of triumphs few, of vain en - deav - ors
out re - gret to go; With gath-ered sheaves we'll meet our bless - ed

point-ment, De - spair, dis - ease or death can nev - er come.
ma - ny, To dust how soon re - turns the mor - tal man.
Sav - ior, Re - joic - ing leave this shad-'wy vale be - low.

CHORUS.

There is a rest for the wea-ry, Sweet rest for the wea-ry, Where

all life's trials, toils and tears shall cease; There is a rest for the wea-ry, Sweet

rest for the wea-ry, A per-fect rest, an ev - er - last-ing peace.

THE VICTORY OF FAITH.

H. F. JAMES.

A. JOEL BOND.

1. As we view the cross of Je-sus, think of all his mer-cy sweet,
2. Tho' oppress'd with fear and doubtings, humbled low by many a fall,
3. For in whom we have be-lieved our hearts do ful-ly, sure-ly know;

Wakes our love for him once sac-ri-ficed; And tho' foes may sore be-
Still our faith and cour-age shall not fail; We shall stand as va-liant
We were blind, but now we know we see! In the midst of pain and

set us, threat-en loud with full de-feat, We shall
sol-diers, march-ing at the Sav-ior's call, We shall
tri-al, he will strength and grace be-stow, For 'tis

con-quer thro' our faith in Christ.
o-ver ev-'ry foe pre-vail.
faith in him brings vic-to-ry.

CHORUS.

We shall con - - quer! we shall
We shall con-quer ev-'ry foe, Christ will

con - - - quer! Faith must still the vic-t'ry win, Sure that
strength and grace be-stow;

162

Je - sus dwells within; We shall con - quer by our faith in him.

159. ON TO CONFLICT.

C. B. M.

CLELAND B. McAFEE, D. D.

1. Christian sol - diers, on to con - flict, Your Cap-tain leads the way;
2. Near at hand and in the dis - tance, There's warfare to be waged;
3. Then a - rise to earn - est ac - tion, And nev - er be dismayed;

The hosts of sin and dark - ness Are read-y for the fray.
For Christ and his re - deemed ones Are 'gainst the foe en-gaged.
Your Lord has prom-ised con - quest, His word was ne'er betrayed.

CHORUS.

Then on! on! on! March on with cour-age true,
Then on, march on, march bold-ly on,

The Lord of our sal - va - tion, Will all your strength re-new.

THE LAND OF BY AND BY.

IDA SCOTT TAYLOR.
QUARTET.

E. S. LORENZ.

1. There is a land, ... a hap-py land, ... Be - yond the
2. There is a robe . . . . . that I shall wear, ... When earth-ly
3. There is a rest . . . . that waits for me— . . . . A peace when

There is a land   a hap-py land,

sun - - ny sky—Where saints and an - - gels praising
toil is o'er; There is a harp . . . . . that I shall
life is done, A ho - ly calm . . . . . from tu-mult

Beyond the sun-ny sky—   Where saints and an -

stand With God, the King most high; A river flows its shores be-
bear, On that ce - les - tial shore; My tongue shall sing the heav'nly
free, Thro' Christ the Savior won; O bless-ed land of by and

gels praising stand   With God, the King most high; A riv - - er

tween, And fields are dressed in fadeless green; No
strain, And praise the Lamb for sinners slain; In
by, My wea - ry soul to thee would fly And

flows its shores between, And fields   are dressed in fadeless green; No

THE LAND OF BY AND BY. Concluded.

land so fair was ev·er seen—. . Sweet land of by and by!
that blest land shall Jesus reign . . Triumphant ev - er - more!
find the home beyond thy sky, . . When I my race have run!

land so fair was ever seen— Sweet land of by and by.

CHORUS.

O beauteous home! for thee I sigh; My soul her spir - it-wings would try

To reach the land beyond the sky—The land of by and by!

161. THY WILL BE DONE. (Chant.)

SIR J. BOWRING.   LOWELL MASON.

Close. Thy will be done!

1 "Thy will be | done!" || In devious way
The hurrying stream of | life may | run;||
Yet still our grateful hearts shall say, |
    "Thy will be | done."

2 "Thy will be | done!" || If o'er us shine
A gladdening and a | prosperous | sun, ||
This prayer will make it more divine— |
    "Thy will be | done!"

3 "Thy will be | done!" || Tho' shrouded o'er
Our | path with | gloom, | one comfort, one
Is ours:—to breathe, while we adore, |
    "Thy will be | done."

CRUSH IT DOWN.

JESSIE H. BROWN.

E. S. LORENZ.

1. Crush the traf-fic out of sight, lift the stand-ard of the right,
2. Crush the traf-fic out of sight, let it sink in deep-est night,
3. Crush the traf-fic out of sight, crush it with Je - ho-vah's might,

Let the weak-er find a broth-er in the strong! (in the strong!)
Let the shad-ow from the hearthstone lift - ed be; (lift-ed be;)
Let the God of bat-tles arm us as we go; (as we go;)

Bid the temp-ter flee a - way 'neath the search-ing light of day,
Let the eyes made dim by tears see the glo - ry thro' the years,
Ho - ly One, 'tis thou a - lone, who hast Sa - tan o - ver-thrown;

And our land be cleansed for - ev - er from the wrong. (from the wrong.)
And the watch-ers chant their psalm of ju - bi - lee. (ju - bi - lee.)
Grant the bless-ing to thy war-ring hosts be - low! (hosts be - low!)

CHORUS.

Crush it down! crush it down! Crush it down! crush it down! 'Tis a

CRUSH IT DOWN. Concluded.

foe whose wiles we know, crush it down! (crush it down!) Boldly crush the traf-fic

out, put its coward force to rout, Crush it down! crush it down! crush it down!

163. WELCOME, BEAUTIFUL MORN.

HAYWARD, 1806.   F. SCHNEIDER.   Arr. by LOWELL MASON, 1841.

1. { Wel-come, de - light-ful   morn ; Thou day of   sa - cred   rest !
     I hail thy kind re - turn, Lord ! make these mo - ments blest ; }

From the low train of   mor-tal toys, I soar to   reach im -

mor-tal joys, I   soar   to   reach   im - mor-tal   joys.

I soar to reach im - mor-tal   joys.

2 Now may the King descend,
    And fill his throne of grace ;
Thy scepter, Lord, extend,
    While saints address thy face !
Let sinners feel thy quickening word,
And learn to know and fear the Lord.

3 Descend, celestial Dove,
    With all thy quickening powers ;
Disclose a Savior's love,
    And bless the sacred hours ;
Then shall my soul new life obtain,
Nor Sabbaths be indulged in vain.

164.

HE IS GOOD.

L. E. J.

L. E. JONES.

1. Let the whole earth praise the Lord, ... For he is
2. To the Lord is hon-or due, ... For he is
3. Bless the Lord, his name a - dore, ... For he is

Praise the Lord,

good,   he is good;   Tell the pow - er
good,   he is good;   Let each heart to
good,   he is good;   Bless and praise him

For he is good,   he is good;

of his word, ... For he is good,   he is
him be true, ... For he is good,   he is
ev - er - more, ... For he is good,   he is

of his word,   For he is good,
him be true,
ev - er - more,

good.   Let each heart re - joice and sing, Let the
good.   To the slave he brings re - lease, To the
good.   Bur-dened souls by care op - pressed, At the

he is good.

HE IS GOOD. Concluded.

cho - rus glad - ly ring, Prais-ing Je - sus Lord and King,
wea - ry bless - ed peace, Bids the cry of sor - row cease,
cross find joy and rest; Sin - ful souls in him are blest,

For he is good, he is good.
For he is good, he is good.

CHORUS.

He is good, he is good, Thro' the
He is good, he is good,

a - ges of e - ter - ni - ty the same; He is good,
He is good,

he is good, Hal - le - lu - jah, let the peo-ple praise his name.
he is good,

SPEAK A KIND WORD.

SOLO OR DUET.
Moderato.

E. L. ASHFORD.

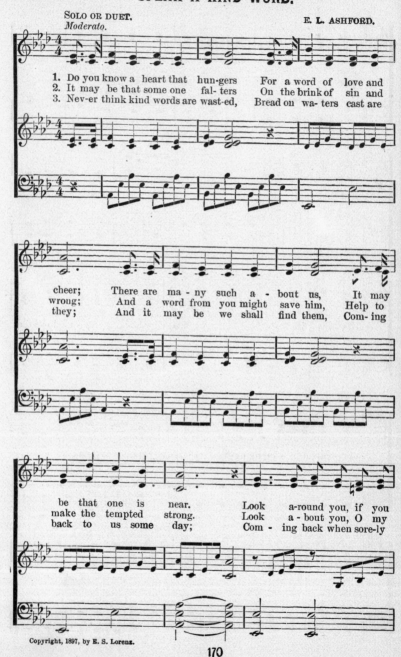

1. Do you know a heart that hun-gers For a word of love and
2. It may be that some one fal- ters On the brink of sin and
3. Nev-er think kind words are wast-ed, Bread on wa- ters cast are

cheer; There are ma - ny such a - bout us, It may
wrong; And a word from you might save him, Help to
they; And it may be we shall find them, Com- ing

be that one is near. Look a-round you, if you
make the tempted strong. Look a - bout you, O my
back to us some day; Com - ing back when sore-ly

SPEAK A KIND WORD. Concluded.

find it,   Speak the word that's need - ed   so;   And your
broth - er!   What a sin is yours and mine,   If we
need - ed,   In a time of sharp dis - tress;   So my

own heart may be strengthened, By the help that you be - stow.
see that help is   need - ed, And we give no friend-ly sign.
friend, let's speak them free-ly, Gift and giv- er God will bless.

CHORUS.

Then speak   a kind word,......Yes, speak a kind word when you can;
Then speak a kind word, speak a kind word,   when you can;

Tho' dark be the day, 'Twill brighten the way, So speak a kind word when you can.

166. GLEAMS FROM THE HOLY LAND.

(For Eight Girls and Primary Class.)

A Song Exercise for Primary Children, or selected scholars. Provide a sandmap, blackboard, or printed map; if possible, all three, as each verse is sung, let the attendants, who have carefully practised their parts, light a little candle on the place designated on the sandmap; pin a gilt star to printed map, make rays with yellow crayon on blackboard map.

E. E. HEWITT.   E. S. LORENZ.

1. There is Bethlehem—put a light; There, one qui-et, star-ry night
3. There's the lake of Gal-i-lee, Je-sus walked up-on the sea;
5. There's Jerusalem—put a light; In the tem-ple, gold and white;
7. There is love-ly Ol-i-vet, Where the light is ling'ring yet;

Je-sus came from heav'n a-bove, Came, the lit-tle child we love.
Stilled the bil-lows by his might, Taught the peo-ple—put a light.
Je-sus gave his Fa-ther's word, Ma-ny there the Gos-pel heard.
Je-sus, ris-ing in the air, Opened heav-en's gates' so fair.

2. There is Nazareth—put a light, Je-sus, like a lil-y white,
4. There's Capernaum—put a light; Je-sus gave the blind their sight,
6. There is Cal-vary, where the light Seemed to end in dark-est night;
8. And his light shines down to-day, We can see it all the way,

Grew, a true, pure-heart-ed boy, Giv-ing all a-round him joy.
Healed the sick and raised the dead, Bless-ings ev-'ry-where he shed.
But from Jos-eph's tomb, close by, Je-sus came, no more to die.
If we fol-low in his love, Grow-ing like our Friend a-bove.

GLEAMS FROM THE HOLY LAND. Concluded.

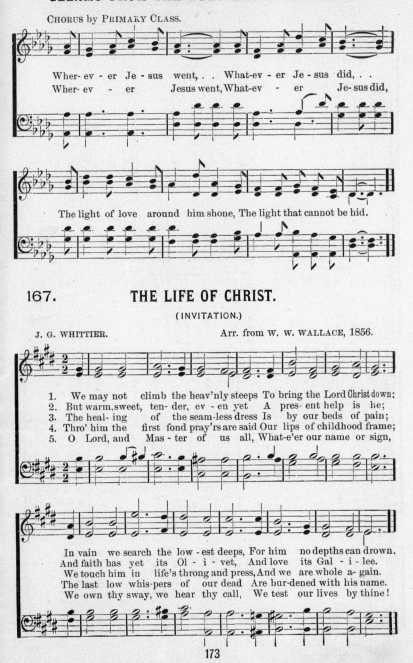

Chorus by PRIMARY CLASS.

Wher-ev-er Je-sus went,.. What-ev-er Je-sus did,..
Wher-ev—er Jesus went, What-ev—er Je-sus did,

The light of love around him shone, The light that cannot be hid.

167.   THE LIFE OF CHRIST.

(INVITATION.)

J. G. WHITTIER.   Arr. from W. W. WALLACE, 1856.

1. We may not   climb the heav'nly steeps To bring the Lord Christ down:
2. But warm, sweet, ten-der, ev-en yet   A pres-ent help is he;
3. The heal-ing   of the seam-less dress Is   by our beds of pain;
4. Thro' him the   first fond pray'rs are said Our lips of childhood frame;
5. O Lord, and   Mas-ter of us all, What-e'er our name or sign,

In vain we search the low-est deeps, For him   no depths can drown.
And faith has yet   its Ol - i - vet, And love   its Gal - i - lee.
We touch him in   life's throng and press, And we are whole a-gain.
The last low whis-pers of   our dead Are bur-dened with his name.
We own thy sway, we hear thy call, We test our lives by thine!

168.

MESSENGERS OF JESUS.

JESSIE H. BROWN.
Unison.

E. S. LORENZ.

1. Mes-sen-gers of Je-sus, ti-dings we are bear-ing, Ti-dings for the
2. Mes-sen-gers of Je-sus, ti-dings we are bear-ing, Ti-dings to the
3. Mes-sen-gers of Je-sus, ti-dings we are bear-ing. Ti-dings for the

lost and hope-less sons of men; He hath come to res - cue,
mourn-ers bowed beneath their cross; He hath come to pit - y,
friend-less, ex - iled and a- lone; He hath come to wel- come—

for your burden car- ing; Hear his spoken promise! look, and live a - gain!
all your sorrows shar-ing, See the glo- ry shining round a-bout the cross!
mansions are pre-par-ing! See his love out-reaching! take him for your own!

FULL CHORUS.   SEMI-CHORUS.   FULL CHORUS.

Je- sus will re-ceive! Tell the news to all the earth! Je-sus will re-ceive!

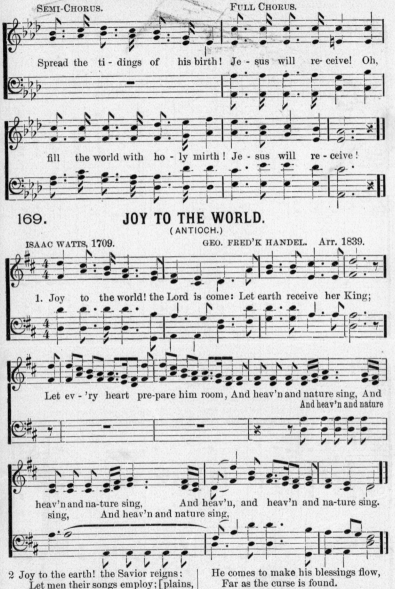

SEMI-CHORUS.

Spread the ti - dings of his birth! Je - sus will re- ceive! Oh,

FULL CHORUS.

fill the world with ho - ly mirth! Je - sus will re - ceive!

169. JOY TO THE WORLD.
(ANTIOCH.)

ISAAC WATTS, 1709.   GEO. FRED'K HANDEL.   Arr. 1839.

1. Joy to the world! the Lord is come: Let earth receive her King;

Let ev - 'ry heart pre-pare him room, And heav'n and nature sing, And
And heav'n and nature

heav'n and na-ture sing,   And heav'n, and heav'n and na-ture sing.
sing,   And heav'n and nature sing,

2 Joy to the earth! the Savior reigns:
Let men their songs employ; [plains,
While fields and floods, rocks, hills, and
Repeat the sounding joy.

3 No more let sins and sorrows grow,
Nor thorns infest the ground;

He comes to make his blessings flow,
Far as the curse is found.

4 He rules the world with truth and grace,
And makes the nations prove
The glories of his righteousness,
And wonders of his love.

170. OLIVET.

IDA BLENKHORN. TENOR AND CONTRALTO. CHAS. H. GABRIEL.

1. Fair Ol - i - vet!
2. From Ol - i - vet
3. O mount of hope,

bright Ol - i - vet, Where oft up - on thy sa - cred brow The Lord with
the Lord a - rose, In maj - es - ty he entered heav'n; With hands out
all glo - ry - crown'd! When faith grows faint I turn to thee, And con - tem -

his dis - ci - ples met— In mem - o - ry I see thee now.
spread to bless the world, This per - fect place to man was giv'n.
plate thy scene di - vine, Oh, bless - ed hour of vic - to - ry.

CHORUS.

Fair Ol - i - vet, ... bright Ol - i - vet, In mem - o -
Fair Ol - i - vet,

Ol - i - vet, ...

OLIVET. Concluded.

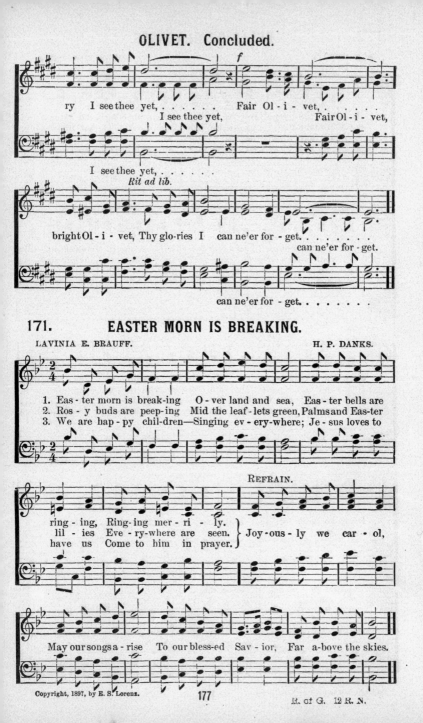

ry I see thee yet, ... Fair Ol - i - vet, ...
I see thee yet,   Fair Ol - i - vet,

I see thee yet, ...

Rit ad lib.

bright Ol - i - vet, Thy glo-ries I can ne'er for - get. . . . . . .
                                    can ne'er for - get.

can ne'er for - get. . . . . . .

171. EASTER MORN IS BREAKING.

LAVINIA E. BRAUFF.   H. P. DANKS.

1. Eas - ter morn is break-ing O - ver land and sea, Eas - ter bells are
2. Ros - y buds are peep-ing Mid the leaf - lets green, Palms and Eas-ter
3. We are hap - py chil-dren—Singing ev - ery-where; Je - sus loves to

REFRAIN.

ring - ing, Ring-ing mer - ri - ly.
lil - ies Eve - ry-where are seen. } Joy-ous - ly we car - ol,
have us Come to him in prayer.

May our songs a - rise To our bless-ed Sav - ior, Far a - bove the skies.

Copyright, 1897, by E. S. Lorenz.   177   R. of G. 12 R. N.

172. BELLS OF GLADNESS.

E. E. HEWITT.   CHAS. EDW. PRIOR.

DUET.

1. Let the joy-ful ti-dings ring in song and sto-ry;
2. Now the hap-py stream-lets from their bond-age break-ing,
3. Shall our lips be si-lent at the cor-o-na-tion
4. Speed the bless-ed mes-sage an-gels brought from heav-en,

Let the bells of glad-ness sweet-ly chime, While the groves and meadows
Mur-mur forth a song of grate-ful praise; Fra-grant buds and blossoms,
Of our all vic-to-rious ris-en King? No, we'll join the cho-rus,
Je-sus lives in glo-ry ev-er-more! Thro' his great a-tone-ment

show the Mas-ter's glo-ry In the joy-ous sun-ny Eas-ter-time.
from their slumber wak-ing, Hail these cheering res-ur-rec-tion days.
pub-lish-ing sal-va-tion; Lov-ing hearts to Je-sus we will bring.
end-less life is giv-en, On the ev-er-last-ing ra-diant shore.

CHORUS.

Ring, ye bells of glad-ness, mer-ri-ly, mer-ri-ly ring; Come, ye

ran-somed peo-ple, cheer-i-ly, cheer-i-ly sing; Light im-mor-tal

BELLS OF GLADNESS. Concluded.

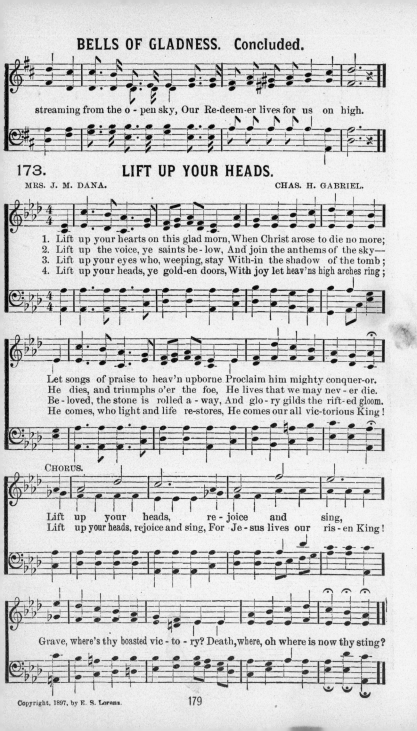

streaming from the o - pen sky, Our Re-deem-er lives for us on high.

173.   LIFT UP YOUR HEADS.

MRS. J. M. DANA.   CHAS. H. GABRIEL.

1. Lift up your hearts on this glad morn, When Christ arose to die no more;
2. Lift up the voice, ye saints be - low, And join the anthems of the sky—
3. Lift up your eyes who, weeping, stay With-in the shadow of the tomb;
4. Lift up your heads, ye gold-en doors, With joy let heav'ns high arches ring;

Let songs of praise to heav'n upborne Proclaim him mighty conquer-or.
He dies, and triumphs o'er the foe, He lives that we may nev - er die.
Be - loved, the stone is rolled a - way, And glo - ry gilds the rift - ed gloom.
He comes, who light and life re-stores, He comes our all vic-torious King!

CHORUS.

Lift up your heads,   re - joice and   sing,
Lift up your heads, rejoice and sing, For Je - sus lives our   ris - en King!

Grave, where's thy boasted vic - to - ry? Death, where, oh where is now thy sting?

THE RETURN OF SPRING.

P. J. OWENS.

E. S. LORENZ.

1. Laughing on the mountains, Smiling in the flow- ers, Sing-ing in the
2. O'er the val-leys straying, Thro' the meadows go - ing. With the lil - ies
3. Walk the fields, fair an- gel, I - cy streams unchaining. Chant thy sweet e-

fount - ains, Blooming in the bow - ers, Break-ing win- try si - lence
play - ing, In the moonshine glowing, Joy and con - so - la - tion
van - gel, Soothe the heart's complaining; From thy deep de- jec - tion

With thy joy- ous wing, Bringer of glad ti-dings, Hail, delightful Spring.
Thou wert made to bring, Like a new creation, God's bright message, Spring.
Earth, a- rise and sing, Hope the res - ur- rec-tion Promised by the Spring.

CHORUS.   8va..............   8va...........loco.

Hail, de-light-ful Spring !   Hail, de-light-ful Spring !

Bring - er of glad ti - dings, Hail, de - light - ful Spring.

175. THE BLESSED DAY.

W. A. M.

W. A. MAY.

1. O Lord, the har-vest of the year, In fruit-ful field and vine,
2. We cast a-broad at thy be-hest, In ti-ny seed, thy word;
3. O Lord, with lov-ing hearts, this day, We sing our prais-es true,

Has yielded free its substance great, Responsive to command of thine.
That, in the sun-shine of thy love, A harvest great may quick afford.
And ask that we may ne'er for-get There's much for us that we can do.

D. S.—*Grant to us, Lord, in la-bor sweet, Thy lov-ing blessing from a-bove.*

The flow-ers sweet of sum-mer fair And fruit-age of the tree,
Throughout our land, the ripe ning fields Are spread in beau-ty fair;
We sow the seed at ear-ly morn, And on throughout life's day,

With wav-ing fields of gold-en grain, Are wel-come gifts from thee.
For thee, O Lord, we seek there-in A gath'ring rich and rare!
From field to field, with pray'r-ful hope, We scat-ter seed al-way.

CHORUS.

D.S.

Oh day of joy— oh day of praise, Oh day of heav'n-ly love!

176. THE BUGLE CALL.

MARK ADAMS.

E. S. LORENZ.

Oh, hear the mer-ry bu-gle call, O'er hill and dale, o'er mountain tall, Call-ing us to re-turn.

1. How bright the hours, when out in the wild-wood stray-ing,
2. In sun-lit field, or for-est with sweet birds sing-ing,

Where God in flow'rs his wis-dom and skill's dis-play-ing,
Where sea doth wield its pow'r, and the foam's wide flinging,

Where soft sweet show'rs are gent-ly our steps de-lay-ing;
We find re-vealed the love that all joy is bring-ing;

D.C.

But from our play We turn a-way, O-bey the bu-gle call.
That love to share Its news to bear, We heed the bu-gle call.

177. THANKS BE TO GOD.

LANTA WILSON SMITH.   GEO. E. MYERS.

1. Thanks be to God for his good-ness, With blessings he crowneth the year,
2. Thanks be to God for his mer-cy; Tho' multitudes slight his commands,
3. Thanks be to God for the Sav-ior; The wonder-ful gift of his love,
4. Thanks be to God for sal-va-tion That brightens the world to-day;

Earth yields her bountiful har-vest, What fragrance and beauty are here.
Still like a fa-ther he loves them, And guides them with bountiful hands.
Souls that are ransomed now praise him, With angels rejoicing a-bove.
Hope of a bless-ed here-af-ter That nev-er will fade a-way.

CHORUS.

Thanks be to God, thanks be to God, Sing ev-'ry heart to-day,

Thanks be to God, thanks be to God, Sing ev-'ry heart to-day.

178.

HE SAVED EVEN ME.

D. C. CARSON.

CHAS. H. GABRIEL.

1. O they sang of a "Land that is fair-er than day," They told of a
2. O they told me "He came from the mansions a-bove;" To save me from
3. Then they said "Whoso-ev-er on him would be-lieve, Should per-ish not,
4. Sin-ner, come un-to him who is a-ble to give A par-don so

kind Fa-ther's care, And they spoke of a Sav-ior "Just o-ver the way,"
sin's dreadful sting; For the sin-burdened soul beat his great heart of love,
but should be saved;" And a peace in the soul they would from him re-ceive;
rich, full and free; O, be-lieve on the Lord and your soul shall then live

Who was wil-ling our bur-dens to bear. Then I said to myself "What
And he longed to him-self all to bring;" Then I asked "Did he die that
'Twas this peace that my soul long had craved; Then I cried "I be-lieve! O
Thro' a bound-less e-ter-ni-ty. Stay no lon-ger a-way, but

is it about—This Je-sus who died on the "tree," And then I cried
I, e-ven I From sin and its curse might be free; And may e-ven
save, Lord, to-day Give peace that comes on-ly from thee; Thy laws I'll o-
come to him now, There's pardon a-wait-ing for thee. I can-not tell

out in my darkness and doubt, "Can he save a poor sin-ner like me?"
I on his mer-cy re - ly—Will he save a poor sin-ner like me?
bey, I will walk in thy way;" Then he saved a poor sin-ner like me.
how, but, if to him you bow, He will save, for he saved e - ven me!

CHORUS.

A sin - ner . . . . like me, ... Can he save a poor
A sin - ner like me, a sin - ner like me,

sin - ner like me? . . . . .

1. And then I cried out in my
2. "And can e - ven I on his
3. "Thy laws I'll o - bey, I will
4. I can - not tell how, but if

a sin - ner like me?

dark-ness and doubt "Can he save a poor sin - ner like me?"
mer - cy re - ly— Will he save a poor sin - ner like me?"
walk in thy way;" Then he saved a poor sin - ner like me!
to him you bow, He will save, for he saved e - ven me.

179. REMEMBER ME.

MRS. E. W. CHAPMAN.

J. H. TENNEY.

1. When wea-ry with . . the tri-als of the day, ...
2. When strong tempta - tion lures my heart to sin
3. When in the shad - ow of the lone-ly vale . . . . . .

1. When wea-ry with the tri-als, with the tri-als of the day,
2. When strong temptation lures my heart to sin, my heart to sin,
3. When in the shad-ow of the lone-ly vale, the lone-ly vale,

And hope's bright light . . . . . no more I see, ...
And no es-cape . . . . from harm I see, ...
I know no grief . . . . . . can come to me; . . . . .

And hope's bright light no more I see, no more I see,
And no es-cape from harm I see, from harm I see,
I know no grief can come to me, can come to me;

This pray'r as-cends . . . to him a-bove the way, ...
'Tis faith that whis - - pers mid the strife and din, ...
Sweet trust shall o - - ver all my fears pre - vail, ...

This pray'r as-cends to him a-bove the way, a-bove the way,
'Tis faith that whispers mid the strife and din, the strife and din,
Sweet trust shall o - ver all my fears pre - vail, my fears pre-vail,

"Dear Lord, ... re - mem - ber me." . . . . .
The Lord . . . . re - mem - bers thee. . . . . . .
The Lord . . . . re - mem - bers me. . . . . . .

"Dear Lord, re - mem - ber me."
The Lord re - mem - bers thee.
The Lord re - mem - bers me.

"Dear Lord, re - mem - ber me, re - mem - ber me."

REMEMBER ME. Concluded.

CHORUS.

Re-mem-ber me, ... re-mem-ber me, ...
Re-mem-ber me, re-mem-ber me,

When to thy king - - - dom thou shalt come; . . .
When to thy kingdom thou shalt come, shalt come;

Remem-ber me, ... re-mem-ber me, ...
Re-mem-ber me, re-mem- ber me,

And take me to . . . . my heavenly home. . . . . . .
And take me to my heavenly, heavenly home.

180.

ALL HAIL.

ANTHEM.

ARTHUR W. NELSON.

1. All hail the pow'r of Je - sus' name, Let an - gels pros-trate fall, Bring
3. Let ev - 'ry kin-dred, ev - 'ry tribe, On this ter-res - trial ball, To

forth the roy - al Di - a - dem, And crown him Lord of all. Crown him ye
him all maj - es - ty as-cribe, And crown him Lord of all. O that with

morn-ing stars of light, Who fixed this earthly ball, Now hail the strength of
yon - der sa-cred throng, We at his feet may fall, We'll join the ev - er -

Israel's might, And crown him Lord of all. Crown him ye morn-ing stars of
last - ing song, And crown him Lord of all. O that with yon-der sa - cred

light, Who fix'd this earthly ball, Now hail the strength of Israel's might, And
throng, We as his feet may fall, We'll join the ev - er-last - ing song, And

ALL HAIL. Concluded.

FINE. f

crown him Lord of all. 2. Ye cho-sen seed of Is-rael's race, Ye ransom'd

from the fall ; Hail him who saves you by his grace, And crown him Lord of all.

ACCOMP.

BASS SOLO. *Slower.*
Sinners, whose love can ne'er for-get The wormwood and the gall, Go

spread your trophies at his feet, And crown him Lord of all, Go

Rit. D. C. 3d verse.
spread your trophies at his feet, And crown him Lord of all.

ROCK OF AGES.

ANTHEM.

W. S. MARTIN.

tears   for - ev - er flow,

Could my tears for — ev-er flow, These for sin could
These for sin   could not a-

not a-tone; Thou must save   and thou a - lone!
tone;   Thou must save   and   thou a - lone!

Noth-ing in   my hand I bring, Sim-ply to   thy cross I

mf   *f*

Nothing in my hand I bring,   Sim-ply to thy cross I

cling; Noth-ing   in   my hand I   bring,   Sim - ply

mf

cling;   Noth-ing   in   my   hand I bring,

to   thy cross I cling.   While I draw   this fleet-ing

p

Sim-ply to   thy   cross I cling.   While I draw this

ROCK OF AGES. Concluded.

breath, When my eye - lids close in death,

pp

fleet-ing breath. When my eye - lids close in death,

cres.

dim.

When I soar to world's unknown, See thee on thy judgment throne,

Rock of A - ges cleft for me, Let me hide myself in thee.

Rock of A - ges cleft for me, Let me hide my-self in thee.

182. THE TIE THAT BINDS.

JOHN FAWCETT. (DENNIS.) HANS GEORGI NAEGELI.

1. Blest be the tie that binds Our hearts in Chris-tian love;
2. Be - fore our Fa - ther's throne, We pour our ar - dent pray'rs;
3. We share our mu - tual woes, Our mu - tual bur - dens bear;
4. When we a - sun - der part, It gives us in - ward pain;

The fel - low - ship of kin - dred minds Is like to that a - bove.
Our fears, our hopes, our aims are one, Our com - forts and our cares.
And oft - en for each oth - er flows The sym - pa - thiz-ing tear.
But we shall still be joined in heart, And hope to meet a - gain.

183. GLORIA PATRI.

CHOIR.

W. J. BALTZELL.

Glo-ry be to the Fa-ther, and to the Son, and to the Ho-ly Ghost, and to the Ho-ly Ghost, As it was in the be-gin-ning, is now, and ev-er shall

FULL CHORUS. *Ritard.*

be, world with-out end, world with-out end. A-men.

184. GLORIA PATRI.

CONGREGATION.

GREGORIAN.

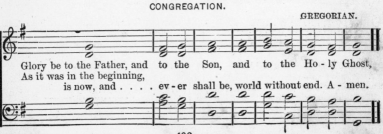

Glory be to the Father, and to the Son, and to the Ho-ly Ghost,
As it was in the beginning,
is now, and . . . . ev-er shall be, world without end. A-men.

CORONATION.

EDWARD PERRONET.

OLIVER HOLDEN.

1. All hail the pow'r of Je-sus' name, Let an-gels prostrate fall;
2. Crown him, ye morn-ing stars of light, Who fixed this earth-ly ball;
3. Let ev-'ry kin-dred, ev-'ry tribe, On this ter-res-trial ball,
4. O that with yon-der sa-cred throng We at his feet may fall!

Bring forth the roy-al di-a-dem, And crown him Lord of all,
Now hail the strength of Is-rael's might, And crown him Lord of all,
To him all ma-jes-ty as-cribe, And crown him Lord of all,
We'll join the ev-er-last-ing song, And crown him Lord of all.

Bring forth the roy-al di-a-dem, And crown him Lord of all.
Now hail the strength of Israel's might, And crown him Lord of all.
To him all ma-jes-ty as-cribe, And crown him Lord of all.
We'll join the ev-er-last-ing song, And crown him Lord of all.

186

THE REDEEMER'S PRAISE.

OH, for a thousand tongues, to sing
  My great Redeemer's praise,
The glories of my God and King,
  The triumphs of his grace.

My gracious Master, and my God,
  Assist me to proclaim—
To spread, through all the earth abroad,
  The honors of thy name.

Jesus! the name that charms our fears,
  That bids our sorrows cease;
'T is music in the sinner's ears,
  'T is life, and health, and peace.

He breaks the power of canceled sin,
  He sets the pris'ner free;
His blood can make the foulest clean—
  His blood availed for me.

M. M. W.   M. M. WELLS.
FINE.

1. Ho - ly Spir - it, faith-ful guide, Ev - er near the Christian's side;
   Gen - tly lead us by the hand, Pil-grims in a des - ert land;

2. Ev - er pres - ent, tru - est friend, Ev - er near thine aid to lend,
   Leave us not to doubt and fear, Grop-ing on in dark-ness drear;

3. When our days of toil shall cease, Wait-ing still for sweet re - lease,
   Noth-ing left but heav'n and pray'r, Wond'ring if our names are there,

D.C.—*Whis-per soft - ly, Wand'rer come! Fol - low me, I'll guide thee home.*

D.C.

Wea - ry souls for e'er re - joice, While they hear that sweet-est voice
When the storms are rag - ing sore, Hearts grow faint, and hopes give o'er,
Wad-ing deep the dis - mal flood, Plead-ing nought but Je - sus' blood,

---

188   JESUS, LOVER OF MY SOUL.

CHARLES WESLEY.   S. D. MARSH.
FINE.

1. Je - sus, Lov - er of my soul, Let me to thy bos - om fly,
   While the near-er wa - ters roll, While the tempest still is high!

D.C.—*Safe in - to the hav - en guide, O re-ceive my soul at last!*

2. Oth - er ref - uge have I none; Hangs my helpless soul on thee:
   Leave, O leave me not a - lone, Still sup-port and com-fort me:

D.C.—*Cov - er my de-fense-less head With the shad-ow of thy wing!*

3. Plenteous grace with thee is found, Grace to cov - er all my sin:
   Let the heal-ing streams abound: Make and keep me pure within.

D.C.—*Spring thou up with - in my heart, Rise to all e - ter - ni - ty.*

Hide me, O my Sav - ior, hide,   Till the storm of life is past;
All my trust on thee is stayed,   All my help from thee I bring;
Thou of life the foun-tain art,   Free - ly let me take of thee:

D.C.

BATTLE HYMN.

English.
Arranged by MRS. G. K. LITTLE.

1. Am I a soldier of the cross, A foll'wer of the Lamb,
And shall I fear to own his cause, Or blush to speak his name?
And when the battle's
And when the battle's

o - ver we shall wear a crown! yes, we shall wear a crown! yes, we shall wear a crown!
o - ver we shall wear a crown! (*Omit 2d and last time.*)

In the new Je - ru - sa - lem! Wear a crown! wear a crown!
Wear a crown! wear a crown!

2 Must I be carried to the skies
  On flow'ry beds of ease,
While others fought to win the prize
And sailed through bloody seas?

3 Are there no foes for me to face?
  Must I not stem the flood?
Is this vile world a friend to grace
To help me on to God?

4 Sure I must fight if I would reign,
  Increase my courage, Lord;
I'll bear the toil, endure the pain,
Supported by thy word.

SALVATION'S FREE.
90
(Key of G.)

1 How sweet the cheering words,
  "Whoever will" may come;
The door of mercy open stands,
As yet there still is room.

Cho.—I'm glad salvation's free!
  I'm glad salvation's free!
Salvation's free for you and me,
I'm glad salvation's free!

2 'Tis the "accepted time,"
  The day of grace and love;
And God invites "whoever will"
His faithfulness to prove.

3 The Saviour sits on high,
  The proof that all is done,
And sinners now God can accept
Through his beloved Son.

DEPTH OF MERCY.
191
(Key of C.)

1 Depth of mercy! can there be
  Mercy still reserved for me?
Can my God his wrath forbear—
Me, the chief of sinners spare?

Cho.—God is love, I know, I feel,
  Jesus weeps, and loves me still.

2 I have long withstood his grace;
  Long provoked him to his face:
Would not hearken to his calls:
Grieved him by a thousand falls.

3 Now incline me to repent;
  Let me now my sins lament;
Now my foul revolt deplore,
Weep, believe, and sin no more.

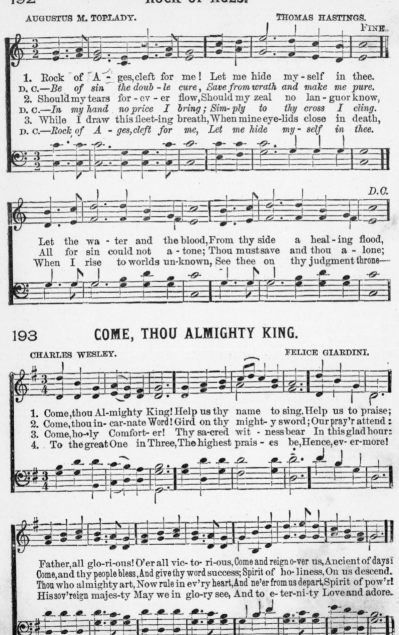

192 ROCK OF AGES.

AUGUSTUS M. TOPLADY.   THOMAS HASTINGS.

FINE.

1. Rock of A - ges, cleft for me! Let me hide my - self in thee.
D. C.—*Be of sin the doub - le cure, Save from wrath and make me pure.*
2. Should my tears for - ev - er flow, Should my zeal no lan - guor know,
D. C.—*In my hand no price I bring; Sim - ply to thy cross I cling.*
3. While I draw this fleet-ing breath, When mine eye-lids close in death,
D. C.—*Rock of A - ges, cleft for me, Let me hide my - self in thee.*

D.C.

Let the wa - ter and the blood, From thy side a heal - ing flood,
All for sin could not a - tone; Thou must save and thou a - lone;
When I rise to worlds un-known, See thee on thy judgment throne—

193 COME, THOU ALMIGHTY KING.

CHARLES WESLEY.   FELICE GIARDINI.

1. Come, thou Al-mighty King! Help us thy name to sing, Help us to praise;
2. Come, thou in - car-nate Word! Gird on thy might - y sword; Our pray'r attend:
3. Come, ho - ly Comfort - er! Thy sa-cred wit - ness bear In this glad hour:
4. To the great One in Three, The highest prais - es be, Hence, ev - er-more!

Father, all glo - ri - ous! O'er all vic - to - ri - ous, Come and reign o - ver us, Ancient of days!
Come, and thy people bless, And give thy word success; Spirit of ho - liness, On us descend.
Thou who almighty art, Now rule in ev'ry heart, And ne'er from us depart, Spirit of pow'r!
His sov'reign majes - ty May we in glo - ry see, And to e - ter-ni - ty Love and adore.

194 THE MERCY-SEAT.
(Key of C.)

FROM every stormy wind that blows,
From every swelling tide of woes,
There is a calm, a sure retreat;
'Tis found before the mercy-seat.

There is a place where Jesus sheds
The oil of gladness on our heads—
A place of all on earth most sweet;
It is the blood-bought mercy-seat.

There is a scene where spirits blend,
Where friend holds fellowship with
    friend;
Though sundered far, by faith they meet
Around one common mercy-seat.

There, there, on eagle wings we soar,
And sin and sense molest no more;
And heaven comes down our souls to greet,
And glory crowns the mercy-seat.

195 REVIVE US AGAIN.
(Key of G.)

WE praise thee, O God! for the Son of
    thy love,
For Jesus, who died and is now gone above.

Cho.—Hallelujah! thine the glory;
    Hallelujah! Amen;
    Hallelujah! thine the glory;
    Revive us again.

All glory and praise to the Lamb that
    was slain,
Who have borne all our sins, and has
    cleansed every stain.

Revive us again; fill each heart with thy
    love;
May each soul be rekindled with fire from
    above.

196 THE GREAT PHYSICIAN.
(Key of E flat.)

THE great Physician now is near,
    The sympathizing Jesus;
He speaks the drooping heart to cheer,
    Oh, hear the voice of Jesus.

Cho.—Sweetest note in seraph song,
    Sweetest name on mortal tongue,
    Sweetest carol ever sung,
    Jesus, blessed Jesus.

Your many sins are all forgiven,
    Oh, hear the voice of Jesus;
Go on your way in peace to heaven,
    And wear a crown with Jesus.

All glory to the dying Lamb!
    I now believe in Jesus;
I love the blessed Savior's name,
    I love the name of Jesus.

197 JESUS PAID IT ALL.
(Key of E flat.)

I HEAR the Savior say,
    Thy strength indeed is small;
Child of weakness, watch and pray,
    Find in me thine all in all.

Cho.—Jesus paid it all,
    All to him I owe;
    Sin had left a crimson stain,
    He washed it white as snow.

For nothing good have I
    Whereby his grace to claim—
I 'll wash my garment white
    In the blood of Calvary's Lamb.

When from my dying bed
    My ransomed soul shall rise,
Then "Jesus paid it all"
    Shall rend the vaulted skies.

198 I GAVE MY LIFE.
(Key of C.)

I GAVE my life for thee,
    My precious blood I shed,
That thou might'st ransomed be,
    And quickened from the dead;
I gave, I gave my life for thee,
What hast thou given for me?

My Father's house of light—
    My glory-circled throne,
I left, for earthly night,
    For wand'rings sad and lone;
I left, I left it all for thee,
Hast thou left aught for me?

And I have brought to thee,
    Down from my home above,
Salvation full and free,
    My pardon and my love;
I bring, I bring rich gifts to thee,
What hast thou brought to me?

199 BLOW YE THE TRUMPET.
(Key of B flat.)

BLOW ye the trumpet, blow
    The gladly solemn sound;
Let all the nations know,
    To earth's remotest bound,
The year of jubilee is come;
Return, ye ransomed sinners, home.

Jesus, our great High Priest,
    Has full atonement made;
Ye weary spirits, rest;
    Ye mourning souls, be glad;
The year of jubilee is come;
Return, ye ransomed sinners, home.

Exalt the Lamb of God,
    The sin-atoning Lamb;
Redemption by his blood
    Through all the world proclaim;
The year of jubilee is come;
Return, ye ransomed sinners, home.

200 ONLY TRUST HIM.
(Key of G.)

COME, every soul by sin oppressed,
    There 's mercy with the Lord,
And he will surely give you rest,
    By trusting in his word.

Cho.—Only trust him, only trust him,
    Only trust him now;
    He will save you, he will save you
    He will save you now.

For Jesus shed his precious blood
    Rich blessings to bestow;
Plunge now into the crimson tide
    That washes white as snow.

Yes, Jesus is the Truth, the Way,
    That leads you into rest;
Believe in him without delay,
    And you are fully blest.

JESUS, SAVIOR, PILOT ME.

REV. EDWARD HOPPER.   J. E. GOULD.

1. Je - sus, Sav - ior, pi - lot me   O - ver life's tempestuous sea;
D. C.—*Chart and com - pass come from thee : Je - sus, Sav - ior, pi - lot me.*
2. As a moth - er stills her child, Thou canst hush the o-cean wild;
D. C.—*Wondrous Sov - 'reign of the sea. Je - sus, Sav - ior, pi - lot me.*
3. When at last I reach the shore, And the fear - ful breakers roar
D. C.—*May I hear thee say to me, "Fear not, I will pi - lot thee!"*

Unknown waves be-fore me roll,   Hid- ing rock and treach'rous shoal:
Boist'rous waves o- bey thy will,   When thou sayst to them, "Be still!"
'Twixt me and the peaceful rest,   Then, while lean- ing on thy breast,

---

MY COUNTRY, 'TIS OF THEE.

SAMUEL F. SMITH.   HENRY CAREY.

1. My country! 'tis of thee, Sweet land of lib - er - ty, Of thee I sing: Land where my
2. My native country, thee,—Land of the noble free,—Thy name—I love; I love thy
3. Let music swell the breeze, And ring, from all the trees, Sweet freedom's song: Let mortal
4. Our fathers' God! to thee, Author of lib- er- ty, To thee we sing: Long may our

fathers died! Land of the pilgrim's pride! From ev'ry mountain side Let freedom ring !
rocks and rills. Thy woods and templed hills: My heart with rapture thrills Like that a- bove.
tongues awake; Let all that breathe partake; Let rocks their silence break—The sound prolong.
land be bright, With freedom's holy light; Protect us by thy might, Great God, our King!

203 CONSECRATION.
(Key of G.)

I AM coming to the cross;
  I am poor, and weak, and blind;
I am counting all but dross,
  I shall full salvation find.

Cho.—I am trusting, Lord, in thee,
  Blest Lamb of Calvary;
  Humbly at thy cross I bow,
  Save me, Jesus, save me now.

Long my heart has sighed for thee,
  Long has evil reigned within.
Jesus sweetly speaks to me,—
  "I will cleanse you from all sin."

Here I give my all to thee,
  Friends, and time, and earthly store,
Soul and body, thine to be—
  Wholly thine for evermore.

204 'T IS DONE.
(Key of G.)

O JESUS, the crucified, now I am free!
  I plunge in the crimson tide opened
    for me.

Cho.—Hallelujah, 'tis done, I believe in
  the Son,
  I am saved by the blood of the cru-
    cified One!

O Jesus, the crucified! now thou art mine,
No longer in dread condemnation I pine.

O Jesus, the crucified! holy and pure,
No wound hath my heart that his blood
  cannot cure.

O'er sin and uncleanness exulting I stand,
And point to the print of the nails in his
  hand.

O Jesus, the crucified! thee will I sing,
My blessed Redeemer, my God, and my
  King.

My soul's filled with joy o'er the victory
  won,
And I'll triumph in death through the
  crucified One.

205 SWEET HOUR OF PRAYER.
(Key of D.)

SWEET hour of prayer! sweet hour of
  prayer!
That calls me from a world of care,
And bids me at my Father's throne
Make all my wants and wishes known:
In seasons of distress and grief,
My soul has often found relief;
And oft escaped the tempter's snare,
By thy return, sweet hour of prayer.

Sweet hour of prayer! sweet hour of prayer!
Thy wings shall my petitions bear
To him whose truth and faithfulness
Engage the waiting soul to bless;
And since he bids me seek his face,
Believe his word, and trust his grace,
I'll cast on him my every care,
And wait for thee, sweet hour of prayer

206 MORE LOVE TO THEE.
(Key of G.)

MORE love to thee, O Christ!
  More love to thee!
Hear thou the prayer I make,
  On bended knee;
This is my earnest plea—
  More love, O Christ, to thee,
    More love to thee!

Once earthly joy I craved,
  Sought peace and rest;
Now thee alone I seek,
  Give what is best:
This all my prayer shall be,—
  More love, O Christ, to thee,
    More love to thee.

207 WHAT A FRIEND.
(Key of F.)

WHAT a friend we have in Jesus,
  All our sins and griefs to bear,
What a privilege to carry
  Everything to God in prayer.
Oh, what peace we often forfeit,
  Oh, what needless pain we bear—
All because we do not carry
  Everything to God in prayer.

Have we trials and temptations?
  Is there trouble anywhere?
We should never be discouraged,
  Take it to the Lord in prayer.
Can we find a friend so faithful,
  Who will all our sorrows share?
Jesus knows our every weakness,
  Take it to the Lord in prayer.

Are we weak and heavy laden,
  Cumbered with a load of care?
Precious Savior, still our refuge,
  Take it to the Lord in prayer.
Do thy friends despise, forsake thee,
  Take it to the Lord in prayer:
In his arms he'll take and shield thee,
  Thou wilt find a solace there.

208 HE LEADETH ME.
(Key of D.)

HE leadeth me, oh, blessed thought,
  Oh, words with heav'nly comfort
    fraught;
Whate'er I do, where'er I be,
Still 't is God's hand that leadeth me.

Ref.—He leadeth me, he leadeth me!
  By his own hand he leadeth me:
  His faithful follower I would be,
  For by his hand he leadeth me.

Sometimes 'mid scenes of deepest gloom,
Sometimes where Eden's bowers bloom,
By waters still, or troubled sea,
Still 't is his hand that leadeth me.

Lord, I would clasp thy hand in mine,
Nor ever murmur or repine—
Content, whatever lot I see,
Since 't is my God that leadeth me.

209 HAMBURG.
(Key of F.)

JUST as I am, without one plea,
  But that thy blood was shed for me,
And that thou bid'st me come to thee,
  O Lamb of God! I come, I come.

Just as I am, and waiting not
To rid my soul of one dark blot,
To thee, whose blood can cleanse each spot
  O Lamb of God! I come, I come.

Just as I am, though tossed about
With many a conflict, many a doubt,
Fightings within, and fears without,
  O Lamb of God! I come, I come.

Just as I am, poor, wretched, blind,
Sight, riches, healing of the mind,
Yea, all I need, in thee to find,
  O Lamb of God! I come, I come.

Arr.

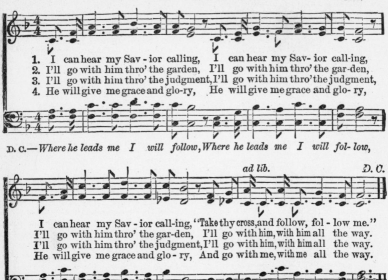

1. I can hear my Sav - ior calling, I can hear my Sav - ior call-ing,
2. I'll go with him thro' the garden, I'll go with him thro' the gar-den,
3. I'll go with him thro' the judgment, I'll go with him thro' the judgment,
4. He will give me grace and glo-ry, He will give me grace and glo-ry,

D. C.—*Where he leads me I will follow, Where he leads me I will fol-low,*

ad lib. D. C.

I can hear my Sav - ior call-ing, "Take thy cross, and follow, fol - low me."
I'll go with him thro' the gar-den, I'll go with him, with him all the way.
I'll go with him thro' the judgment, I'll go with him, with him all the way.
He will give me grace and glo - ry, And go with me, with me all the way.

Where he leads me I will fol-low; I'll go with him, with him all the way.

211 REMEMBER ME.
(Key of F.)

ALAS! and did my Savior bleed?
  And did my Sov'reign die?
Would he devote that sacred head
  For such a worm as I?

CHO.—Help me, dear Savior, thee to own,
  And ever faithful be;
And when thou sittest on thy throne,
  O Lord, remember me.

Was it for crimes that I have done
  He groaned upon the tree?
Amazing pity! grace unknown!
  And love beyond degree!

Thus might I hide my blushing face,
  While his dear cross appears,
Dissolve my heart in thankfulness,
  And melt mine eyes to tears.

But drops of grief can ne'er repay
  The debt of love I owe;
Here, Lord, I give myself away;
  'T is all that I can do.

212 NETTLETON.
(Key of E flat.)

COME, thou Fount of every blessing,
  Tune my heart to sing thy grace;
Streams of mercy, never ceasing,
  Call for songs of loudest praise.

Teach me some melodious sonnet,
  Sung by flaming tongues above;
Praise the mount—I'm fixed upon it—
  Mount of thy redeeming love.

Here I'll raise mine Ebenezer;
  Hither by thy help I'm come;
And I hope, by thy good pleasure,
  Safely to arrive at home.
Jesus sought me when a stranger,
  Wandering from the fold of God;
He, to rescue me from danger,
  Interposed his precious blood.

213 MY JESUS, I LOVE THEE.
(Key of F.)

MY Jesus, I love thee, I know thou art
    mine;
For thee all the follies of sin I resign;
My gracious Redeemer, my Savior art
    thou;
If ever I loved thee, my Jesus, 't is now.

I love thee, because thou hast first loved
    me,
And purchased my pardon on Calvary's
    tree;
I love thee for wearing the thorns on thy
    brow;
If ever I loved thee, my Jesus, 't is now.

214 I LOVE THY KINGDOM, LORD.
(Key of C.)

I LOVE thy kingdom, Lord,
The house of thine abode,
The Church our blest Redeemer saved
With his own precious blood.

I love thy Church, O God!
Her walls before thee stand,
Dear as the apple of thine eye,
And graven on thy hand.

Beyond my highest joy
I prize her heavenly ways,
Her sweet communion, solemn vows,
Her hymns of love and praise.

Sure as thy truth shall last,
To Zion shall be given
The brightest glories earth can yield,
And brighter bliss of heaven.

215 TURN TO THE LORD.
(Key of G.)

COME, ye sinners, poor and needy,
Weak and wounded, sick and sore;
Jesus ready stands to save you,
Full of pity, love, and pow'r.

CHO.—Turn to the Lord, and seek salvation,
Sound the praise of his dear name;
Glory, honor, and salvation,
Christ the Lord has come to reign.

Now, ye needy, come and welcome,
God's free bounty glorify;
True belief and true repentance,
Every grace that brings you nigh.

Let not conscience make you linger,
Nor of fitness fondly dream;
All the fitness he requireth
Is to feel your need of him.

Come, ye weary, heavy laden,
Bruised and mangled by the fall;
If ou tarry till you 're better,
You will never come at all.

216 BALERMA.
(Key of B flat.)

COME, Holy Spirit, heavenly Dove,
With all thy quick'ning powers;
Kindle a flame of sacred love
In these cold hearts of ours.

Dear Lord! and shall we ever live
At this poor dying rate,
Our love so faint, so cold to thee,
And thine to us so great?

Come, Holy Spirit, heavenly Dove,
With all thy quick'ning powers;
Come shed abroad a Savior's love,
And that shall kindle ours.

217 BALERMA.
(Key of B flat.)

OH, for a closer walk with God,
A calm and heavenly frame;
A light to shine upon the road
That leads me to the Lamb.

Return, O holy Dove, return,
Sweet messenger of rest;
I hate the sins that made thee mourn,
And drove thee from my breast.

The dearest idol I have known,
Whate'er that idol be,
Help me to tear it from thy throne,
And worship only thee.

218 BOYLSTON.
(Key of C.)

A CHARGE to keep I have,
A God to glorify,
A never-dying soul to save
And fit it for the sky.

Arm me with jealous care
As in thy sight to live,
And, oh, thy servant, Lord, prepare
A strict account to give.

Help me to watch and pray
And on thyself rely,
Assured, if I my trust betray,
I shall forever die.

219 HAPPY DAY.
(Key of G.)

OH, happy day that fixed my choice
On thee, my Savior and my God;
Well may this glowing heart rejoice,
And tell its raptures all abroad.

CHO.—Happy day! happy day!
When Jesus washed my sins away;
He taught me how to watch and pray
And live rejoicing every day.
Happy day! Happy day!
When Jesus washed my sins away.

'T is done—the great transaction 's done;
I am my Lord's and he is mine;
He drew me, and I followed on,
Rejoiced to own the call divine.

Now rest—my long divided heart—
Fixed on this blissful center, rest;
Here I have found a nobler part,
Here heavenly pleasures fill my breast.

220 NO SORROW THERE.
(Key of G.)

OH, sing to me of heaven,
When I am called to die;
Sing songs of holy ecstasy,
To waft my soul on high.

CHO.—‖:There 'll be no more sorrow there,:‖
In heaven above,
Where all is love,
There 'll be no more sorrow there.

When the last moments come,
Oh, watch my dying face,
To catch the bright seraphic gleam
Which on each feature plays.

Then to my raptured ear
Let one sweet song be given;
Let music cheer me last on earth,
And greet me first in heaven!

221 COME, HOLY GHOST.
(Key of G.)

COME, Holy Ghost, in love,
Shed on us from above
Thine own bright ray!
Divinely good thou art;
Thy sacred gifts impart
To gladden each sad heart:
Oh, come to-day!

Come, tenderest Friend, and best,
Our most delightful Guest,
With soothing power:
Rest, which the weary know,
Shade, 'mid the noontide glow,
Peace, when deep griefs o'erflow,
Cheer us this hour!

222 **NEW HAVEN.**
(Key of G.)

MY faith looks up to thee,
  Thou Lamb of Calvary;
Savior divine:
Now hear me while I pray;
Take all my guilt away;
Oh, let me, from this day,
  Be wholly thine.

May thy rich grace impart
Strength to my fainting heart;
  My zeal inspire;
As thou hast died for me,
Oh, may my love to thee
Pure, warm, and changeless be—
  A living fire.

223 **ST. THOMAS.**

OH, bless the Lord, my soul!
  Let all within me join,
And aid my tongue to bless his name
  Whose favors are divine.

Oh, bless the Lord, my soul,
  Nor let his mercies lie
Forgotten in unthankfulness,
  And without praises die.

'Tis he forgives thy sins—
  'Tis he relieves thy pain—
'Tis he that heals thy sicknesses,
  And gives thee strength again.

224 **LABAN.**
(Key of C.)

MY soul, be on thy guard:
  Ten thousand foes arise;
The hosts of sin are pressing hard
  To draw thee from the skies.

Oh, watch, and fight, and pray;
  The battle ne'er give o'er;
Renew it boldly every day,
  And help divine implore.

Ne'er think the vict'ry won,
  Nor lay thy armor down;
Thy arduous work will not be done
  Till thou obtain thy crown.

Fight on, my soul, till death
  Shall bring thee to thy God;
He'll take thee, at thy fleeting breath,
  Up to his blest abode.

225 **LET THE SAVIOR IN.**
(Key of A.)

BEHOLD a stranger at the door!
  He gently knocks, has knocked before,
Has waited long, is waiting still;
  You treat no other friend so ill.

CHO.—Oh, let the dear Savior come in,
  He'll cleanse thy heart from sin;
  Oh, keep him no more out at the door,
But let the dear Savior come in.

Oh, lovely attitude!—he stands
With melting heart and loaded hands;
Oh, matchless kindness!—and he shows
This matchless kindness to his foes.

But will he prove a friend indeed?
He will,—the very Friend you need;
The Friend of sinners,—yes, 'tis he,
With garments dyed on Calvary.

Rise, touched with gratitude divine,
Turn out his enemy and thine,—
That soul-destroying monster, sin,—
And let the heavenly Stranger in.

226 **FULL CONSECRATION.**
(Key of D.)

TAKE my life, and let it be
  Consecrated, Lord, to thee;
Take my hands and let them move
At the impulse of thy love.

CHO.—Wash me in the Savior's precious blood,
  Cleanse me in its purifying flood;
  Lord, I give to thee my life and all, to be
  Thine, henceforth, eternally.

Take my moments and my days,
Let them flow in endless praise;
Take my intellect, and use
Every power as thou shalt choose.

Take my love; my Lord, I pour
At thy feet its treasure-store!
Take myself, and I will be
Ever, only, all for thee!

227 **HOW I LOVE JESUS.**
(Key of A flat.)

HOW sweet the name of Jesus sounds
  In a believer's ear;
It soothes his sorrows, heals his wounds,
  And drives away his fear.

CHO.—Oh, how I love Jesus,
  Oh, how I love Jesus,
  Oh, how I love Jesus,
    Because he first loved me.

It makes the wounded spirit whole,
  And calms the troubled breast;
'T is manna to the hungry soul,
  And to the weary, rest.

Dear name, the rock on which I build,
  My shield and hiding-place;
My never-failing treasure, filled
  With boundless stores of grace.

228 **I DO BELIEVE.**
(Key of G.)

FATHER, I stretch my hands to thee;
  No other help I know;
If thou withdraw thyself from me,
  Ah, whither shall I go?

CHO.—I do believe, I now believe,
  That Jesus died for me,
  And thro' his blood, his precious blood,
  I shall from sin be free.

What did thine only Son endure
  Before I drew my breath!
What pain, what labor, to secure
  My soul from endless death!

Author of faith, to thee I lift
  My weary, longing eyes;
Oh, may I now receive that gift;
  My soul, without it, dies.

229 **LENOX.**
(Key of B flat.)

ARISE, my soul, arise!
  Shake off thy guilty fears;
The bleeding Sacrifice
  In my behalf appears;
Before the throne my Surety stands,
My name is written on his hands.

My God is reconciled,
  His pard'ning voice I hear;
He owns me for his child,
  I can no longer fear;
With confidence I now draw nigh,
And Father, Abba, Father, cry.

TOPICAL INDEX.

The songs are indexed with reference to their secondary as well as their primary significance. Except in the case of standard hymns, the index is that of *titles*.

GENERAL INDEX.

Titles in small capitals.   First lines in Roman.

207